PEAK DISTRICT TREASURE HUNTS

Mystery Tours on Foot & by Car

Ian Almond

Published by Sigma Leisure – an imprint of
Sigma Press, 5 Alton Road, Wilmslow, Cheshire SK9 5DY, England.

British Library Cataloguing in Publication Data
A CIP record for this book is available from the British Library.

ISBN: 1-85058-810-4

Typesetting and Design by: Sigma Press, Wilmslow, Cheshire.

Cover photograph: Overlooking Eyam from the north *(Ian Almond)*

Maps, photographs and illustrations: Ian Almond; maps reproduced from Ordnance Survey based mapping on behalf of The Controller of Her Majesty's Stationery Office © Crown Copyright 2004 100032058

Printed by: Interprint Ltd, Malta

Disclaimer: the information in this book is given in good faith and is believed to be correct at the time of publication. No responsibility is accepted by either the author or publisher for errors or omissions, or for any loss or injury howsoever caused. Only you can judge your own fitness, competence and experience. Do not rely solely on sketch maps for navigation: we strongly recommend the use of appropriate Ordnance Survey (or equivalent) maps.

Preface

Have you ever wanted to go on a mystery tour in beautiful surroundings? This book contains 16 such tours in the form of treasure hunts within the Peak District National Park. They were originally set for a website, but have been adapted and brought up to date for this book.

Each treasure hunt involves solving clues, the answers to which can be found on location; each answer leads to the next place to continue the hunt. In this way the "hunter" is taken on a trip through an area of the Peak District until reaching the destination. The hunts are not easy; therefore to ensure that the "hunter" can always reach their destination, the answers to each clue are shown in a solutions section at the back of the book, together with photographs and maps where appropriate.

At the front of the book there is an overall map of the Peak District showing the locations of the hunts. The reader can pick a hunt in the area of their choice, turn to the page where the hunt commences and follow it to its conclusion.

At the beginning of each hunt, there are brief instructions regarding the terrain and walking distances to enable users to pick the appropriate hunt for the day.

A vital part of this activity is the use of Ordnance Survey maps, and the following ones are required to complete all of the hunts:

Ordnance Survey Explorer (or Outdoor Leisure) 1

Ordnance Survey Explorer (or Outdoor Leisure) 24

Every effort has been made to ensure the accuracy of the "on the ground" detail, and at the time of going to press the author believes the details of each hunt to be accurate. However, over the passage of time house names (a common clue) may change, roads may become one-way and signs may be moved. In short, the clues for the hunts may become compromised. The solution section at the back of the book will show the answers for those clues even if they no longer exist, so the "hunter" can get back on track where this may happen.

Finally, please respect the privacy of the villagers and farmers throughout the hunts, and follow the country code when in open land. There is no need to go onto any private land for any of the hunts; if you find yourself doing so, you have taken the wrong turn! Check the solution for that hunt to get back on the right track.

Ian Almond

Contents

THE HUNTS

SOLUTIONS

Introduction

This book has been developed from a website devoted to occasional treasure hunts: "The Peak District Treasure Hunt" (web address: www.peaktreasurehunt.com)

All of the treasure hunts within the book have been completed (and won) by members of the public. They logged onto the website, printed out the clues, ventured out into the Peak District, followed the hunt and eventually located a treasure codeword that was hidden just before each hunt took place.

There are now no treasure codewords to find and no prizes to claim. However, the treasure hunts themselves remain valid (excepting for unforeseeable changes to physical fixtures).

To enable the crafting of a treasure hunt without putting down paper clues, a series of methods has been developed and each one is explained in the "Solving different types of clue" section. Some of these methods can be a little contrived, but remain valid nevertheless, if they are followed correctly and to the letter. They all use physical features (e.g. horizon clues) and permanent fixtures (pubs, churches etc) to create the clues.

Some of the clues are fairly simple; others will require keen observation or occasional lateral thinking. Therefore there is a Solutions section in the back half of the book. It is recommended that you use two bookmarks whenever you do a hunt: one to keep the page of the hunt and the other to refer to the solution. *(Note that the page number of the solution is clearly indicated in the introduction to each walk.)*

The maps shown at the end of each hunt's solution are only sketch maps and lots of detail is missed out. The accuracy of them cannot be guaranteed. However, they should be clear enough for you to work out where the hunts progressed, if used in conjunction with the Ordnance Survey maps on which all the given grid references are based.

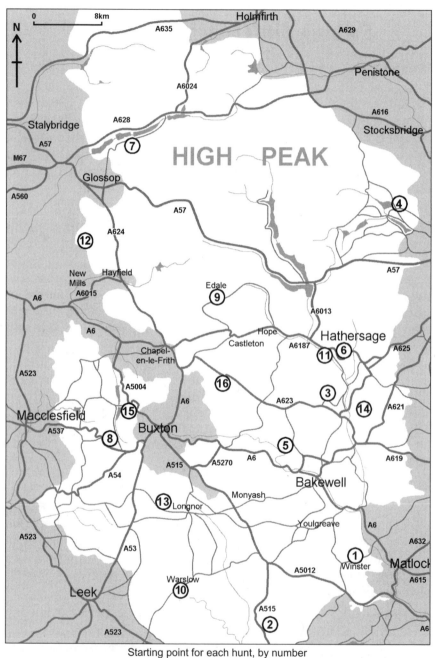

Starting point for each hunt, by number

Solving different types of clue

Word Grids

These are made up of a series of clues where the answers exactly fit the spaces within a grid, as shown below. Note that all spaces and punctuation are omitted from the answers. When the grid is completed, the highlighted column shows the answer, which is typically the next destination, in this case EDALE.

Clue 3			R	O	S	E	C	O	T	T	A	G	E
Clue 2			M	I	L	L	D	A	L	E		
Clue 5			S	T	M	A	R	Y	S			
Clue 4	T	H	E	S	C	H	O	O	L	H	O	U	S	E
Clue 1			E	M	I	L	Y					

Grid References

These will always be given as per the Ordnance Survey standard, i.e. two leading letters and a six-digit number. Each combination of leading letters defines a very large area of 100km x 100km, which is more than the total area of the Peak District. For all but a few grid references given within this book, the leading letters are SK.

The six-digit number is made up of the first three digits defining an easting (counted eastwards from a fixed position) and the following three digits defining a northing (counted northwards from a fixed position). They show a location to within a 100m square on one or other of the two Ordnance Survey maps described in the Preface. As an example, the OS grid reference SK265707 is made up of:

❖ Leading letters SK

❖ Easting of 265

❖ Northing of 707

To locate this grid reference, look along the top of the Ordnance Survey Outdoor Leisure 24 (or Explorer 24) map to an easting of 26 and 5 tenths then count up the side of the map to a northing of 70 and 7 tenths. In this example you should locate a small square around Chatsworth House hunting tower.

Codewords

To solve these, remove the letters in your discovered phrase one by one from the given codeword. When removing the phrase from a codeword, always remove the very next occurrence of the letters in order, to ensure the remaining words are correct. There may be dummy letters at the start and the end of the clue to further disguise the answer.

For example: remove the discovered phrase "The Old Rectory" from Codeword 1 below:

Codeword 1: TCHEHOATLSDWRORECTTHOHORUSYE

Removing T HE O L D R   ECT   O   R   Y

Leaves   C H AT S W OR   TH HO US E

So the answer is – CHATSWORTH HOUSE.

Word Finder Squares

In this type of clue, answers to a list of questions on the treasure hunt route are found on a square grid of letters and are crossed out leaving some sort of description to be followed. Answers can be read across, down and diagonally from left to right. Alongside is an example. In this square, the five clue answers were WINDMILL, ST JOHNS, RED LION, PAUL MOSS, HORSES.

W	S	T	J	O	H	N	S
C	I	O	U	N	T	N	H
T	E	N	N	P	O	A	O
C	E	S	D	I	N	O	R
P	A	U	L	M	O	S	S
R	T	D	H	F	I	R	E
O	E	M	T	H	E	L	S
R	T	R	E	E	G	D	L

Removing the answers to the clues leaves, in this case, the slogan "COUNT TEN PACES NORTH FROM THE TREE". There may be spare letters (in this case GD at the end of the slogan).

Primary Digits

To find the Primary Digit of a several digit number (typically a four-digit year), proceed as follows.

❖ Add up the digits of the number.

❖ If the answer is a one-digit number, this is the primary digit.

❖ If the answer has more than one digit, proceed to add up the digits of this number, and so on until you reach a one-digit answer.

For example, the primary digit of "1869" is worked out as follows:

$1 + 8 + 6 + 9 = 24.$

$2 + 4 = 6.$

Therefore, the primary digit of 1869 is 6.

Word Search

This is where an instruction, usually directions to the next clue, is hidden within a grid by changing the direction of the writing. The "hunter" is given the starting co-ordinate, and the instruction is formed by moving from letter to letter in any direction except diagonal. Words are joined by a line instead of spaces, which could be straight or L-shaped, to show where one word finishes and another word starts. Every letter in the grid is used only once and no words within the instruction found are shortened. Square blocks are just fillers.

A solved example is shown here, the arrows following the direction of text. Starting from grid position 4 across and 5 down, the instructions read:

	1	2	3	4	5	6	7	8	9
1	B	A	N	U	R	E	H		
2	R	■	K	O	O	O	A	C	T
3	E	U	Y	T	F	E	H		
4	V	N	L	B	R	I	■		
5	I	T	I	T	U	R	D	G	E
6	R	r	D	N	N	■	r	A	
7	H	E	F	■	A	I	■	T	T
8	T	L	O	E	L	E	F	I	
9	I	L	R	E	■	A	T	■	T
10	W	O	T	L	L	L	E	H	

"TURN LEFT AT THE TALL TREE AND FOLLOW THE RIVERBANK UNTIL YOU REACH THE FOOTBRIDGE."

Key Counted Hidden Clues

To solve this kind of clue requires great care. You are given the "counting key" and you have to find the hidden clue from a discovered text (e.g. a manuscript or plaque) by picking out letters according to that counting key.

When a number is given, count through the text *starting from the current position* to pick the next letter in the clue. Whenever a letter is given, put it in directly. If, while counting, you reach the end of the source text and you still have more numbers left in the key, "wrap around" to the beginning of the text again. Spaces and punctuation are not included in the counting.

When solving these types of clue, you must be very careful to count the letters accurately because if at any time you miscount, the whole of the rest of the message will become nonsense. The best way to do this is to copy down the whole text carefully first of all, then mark your position as you go along. Therefore, when faced with any of these clues, take a pencil and paper with you.

Here is an example of this type of clue. The text to read is:

The evocative bubbling call of the Curlew is a characteristic sound of the moorlands in summertime.

The counting key –

1, 13, r, 5, 4, 6, f, 16, a, 5, 10, 1, 1, 7, 9, x, 2, r, 9, 2, d.

Translates to this solution:

t, u, r, n, l, e, f, t, a, t, t, h, e, n, e, x, t, r, o, a, d.

In the example above, the first letter is found by counting 1, as indicated by the first number in the counting key, from the start of the text (giving the first letter, "t"). The next number in the counting key is 13. Counting 13 from the "t" takes us to the letter "u", then the letter "r" is given for free in the key. The next count is 5, taken from where the last letter ("u") was found, which leads to the letter "n". The counting continues until the counting key is completed to reveal the solution above, in this case "wrapping round" to the beginning of the text again for the last three letters.

Bearing and Range

Bearings are given in degrees from 0 to 359 with 0 = due north, 90 = due east, 135 = due south-east and so on. The range will be in kilometres unless otherwise stated. The diagram shows that Hulme End is 2.7km from Hartington, at a bearing of 250 degrees.

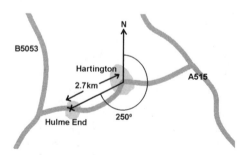

Reproduced from Ordnance Survey based mapping on behalf of The Controller of Her Majesty's Stationery Office © Crown Copyright 2004 100032058

Codeworded Ciphers

This routine is only used in hunts 7, 9, 11, 12 and 14. A special code-word – the "cipher codeword" – is used to break the cipher in the following manner:

The inner wheel (see overleaf) is turned against the outer wheel such that the first letter in the cipher codeword (on the inner wheel) is lined up with the 'A' on the outer wheel. Then you must find the first letter of the encoded text on the outer wheel and read the decoded letter, which is next to it on the inner wheel. Then proceed by lining up the second letter of the cipher codeword (on the inner wheel) with the 'A' on the outer wheel, find the second letter of the encoded text on the outer wheel and read the decoded letter next to it on the inner wheel, and so on.

For example, using the codeword "JORDAN" to decode "UUP", the 'J' on the inner wheel is placed next to the 'A' on the outer wheel and the 'U' on the outer wheel is decoded to a 'D' (on the inner wheel).

For the next letter, the 'A' on the outer wheel is placed alongside the 'O' on the inner wheel and the 'U' on the outer wheel is decoded to 'I' (on the inner wheel).

For the third letter, the 'A' on the outer wheel is placed alongside the 'R' on the inner wheel and the 'P' on the outer wheel is decoded to 'G' (on the inner wheel).

In this example, the coded message "UUP", when decoded with the cipher codeword "JORDAN", becomes "DIG". The cipher codeword is simply repeated to decode longer messages (e.g. JORDANJORDANJOR).

You will need to copy the following page, for which permission is granted. Cut out the two wheels from the photocopy and glue them onto rigid card. Make a hole in the centre of each, place the inner wheel on top of the outer wheel and push a split pin through the centre.

CIPHER WHEEL

- Align each letter of the codeword in turn with the letter "A" on the outer disk.
- Find each letter of the cipher in turn on the outer wheel.
- Read each deciphered letter in turn on the inner wheel.

The inner wheel for the cipher codewheel

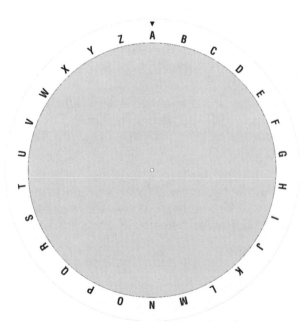

The outer wheel for the cipher codewheel

THE HUNTS

A church, a post and a grassy slope – can you solve the question in Hunt 10?

Hunt I: Winster

Map: Ordnance Survey Explorer 24 or Outdoor Leisure 24.

Starting point: Winster Market House, found at OS grid reference SK242606.

Terrain: Around 4km walking, little of which is off-road.

Duration: Around 3 hours.

Solution: page 60

Starting from Winster Market House *(closed during British Wintertime)*:

Clue 1 is the name of the nearby house **where you can read the leaves**. **Clue 2** is the house on the main road to the east whose name perhaps **sent fear** through those who dreaded Stan's release.

Follow the road uphill adjacent to Winster Market House. **Clue 3** is the name of this road. Continue and fill in the rest of the words to link to the next place.

Clue 4 is the first name of one of the houses – you might find it on a breakfast table. Continue up the road for a while until the road splits. Take the right fork, all the time looking for **Clue 5**, which is the first name of a house where Winnie The Pooh might like to live. Keep on until you reach a flight of steps on the left. Go up them and locate a house named after a mammal. The first name of the house is **Clue 6**.

Keep going up to the T-junction and turn right, still going uphill. After about 50 metres take the path downhill to the right until you reach a chapel on the left. Follow down the footpath next to the chapel and you will reach a road on which you can see a cottage with a collection of different-sized animal skulls on the side wall. The first two words of the name of this cottage is **Clue 7**.

Follow this same road to the west until the road forks. Take the right fork until you reach a row of cottages accessed by a path on the left of the main one. Take this path. The last cottage is named after a tree. The tree name is **Clue 8**.

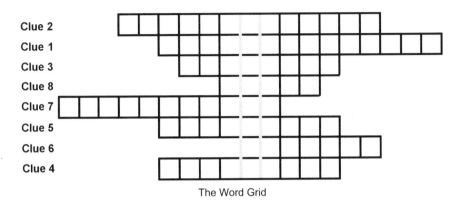

Clue 2
Clue 1
Clue 3
Clue 8
Clue 7
Clue 5
Clue 6
Clue 4

The Word Grid

Now read down the highlighted column on the Word Grid, to find the name of the next destination in the hunt. When you reach this destination look for the original date stone above the side door. Use this to find the next place to take up the treasure hunt as follows:

Year on date stone:
multiply by 100:
add 44843: _+ 44843_
leaves OS Grid Ref SK

Use the OS map to locate the position, which should be close to the centre of a Peak District village. If not, re-check the date and your calculation.

In the next section, you will find clues as you go along which are in the Word Finder Square on page 13, written horizontally, vertically or diagonally. Cross out the letters of these words as you find them to reveal a hidden message, finally locating the treasure from the point where the descriptive section finishes. (An example is on page 4 of this book.)

Continuing at the new location, you need to look for **the name of a 19th-century water-related monument**, (both words of one of its 2 possible names are on the monument itself and are separately found in the Word Finder Square below). Close to here you will see **a white building with an oval name plaque above the door**. (Also in the Word Finder Square.) From this point take the road east until you reach the building **where the high time started in 1870**. (The building's name is in the Word Finder Square.) Look around this building for **where the 6th of 10 is arguably the most important** (also in the Word Finder Square).

Nearby is a stone and grass war memorial. Write down the last date written on the stone tablet in front of this memorial as Date 1 below:

Date 1: _____

Proceed down the main street next to this building in a westerly direction. Take the left fork at the monument and stay on the main road for a while until you see a building on the right with a date stone showing (in a very unusual way) a date exactly 100 years before Date 1. The **first word in the building name** is also in the Word Finder Square. Now turn down the road you have just passed on the left.

Follow this narrow road until you reach an area where the road finishes and a downhill path commences. Go down the path and you will see a cottage (**first two words of name** in Word Finder Square) with a rickety bench in front. Pass on down the path to the left and continue down the steps to the bottom of the hill. (Watch out for the geese)! Go up the road to the left, passing a café with a sign showing some words in the Word Finder Square which are, apparently, "the rule of the road". Continue up the road until you reach two benches on the left. There is a named building opposite the benches, which **could have been built at 327**. The first two words of this building's name are in the Word Finder Square. Go down the road to the right of this building (road name in Word Finder Square) and take the path at the end of the road.

Squeeze through the stile into a field and follow the path past a bench touchingly dedicated to someone with a phrase reminiscent of a pop song (**the pop group's name** is in the Word Finder Square). When the path meets another, carry on in the same direction until you go through the gate. Turn left up the road past the telephone box. After 60-70m there is a path on the right in front of a row of cottages. Go along this path. There is a small conservatory in front of one of the cottages (**cottage name** in Word Finder Square).

Follow the path until you reach the road (look about for **the named letter box** in Word Finder Square). There is a lone cottage in view

W	A	F	T	C	R	O	O	K	E	D	S	T	I	C	K
O	E	R	A	T	I	G	H	T	U	B	E	H	N	D	T
O	W	E	S	L	E	Y	A	N	R	E	F	O	R	M	E
D	B	I	N	T	H	E	R	I	U	V	E	U	R	I	A
S	A	S	A	S	B	M	A	G	L	L	W	S	O	L	S
I	N	O	D	E	B	R	A	E	M	A	R	H	L	N	W
D	K	W	R	E	I	E	O	R	C	L	O	A	S	E	I
E	S	B	Y	O	L	I	S	O	A	T	H	L	E	N	T
V	I	F	O	N	C	O	C	T	K	E	C	T	L	I	H
I	D	F	A	F	T	K	H	O	L	L	E	N	T	R	H
E	E	M	E	A	S	U	H	B	N	R	E	O	E	W	O
W	U	A	S	H	I	D	M	A	D	D	E	T	N	I	V
H	N	P	R	I	M	I	T	I	V	E	U	K	O	T	I
H	E	R	O	O	H	E	A	D	T	E	S	I	O	N	S
F	A	T	R	T	E	E	G	R	O	W	N	L	T	I	N
G	O	A	L	L	S	A	I	N	T	S	N	L	I	T	X

The Word Finder Square

named after a Caledonian place (**first word of cottage name** in Word Finder Square). Go down the public bridleway, past the cottage and over the small bridge. From here you can see a bench **which should never get rained on**, in honour of the man with the _____ (**rest of phrase** in Word Finder Square). Go down the main path to the left of the bench and keep going until you reach a swing gate and a stile. Go through the stile and follow the path.

Now read the remaining text in the Word Finder Square to complete the hunt.

Hunt 2: Tissington

Map: Ordnance Survey Explorer 24 or Outdoor Leisure 24.

Starting point: Tissington Hall, found at OS grid reference SK175523.

Terrain: Around 4km walking, some of which is off-road. Sure-footedness will be required in part of the hunt.

Duration: Around 4 hours.

Solution: page 64

This hunt commences with a verse:

> Within spitting distance of Tissington Hall,
> Look for a weather vane atop a gold ball.
> Now look for a well that's shallow and wide
> And follow the stream which flows from its side.

Follow the path of the stream as it goes down a culvert and reappears across the road. It goes down another culvert at which point you should look for a nearby notice board which has a dedication to someone. Standing with your back to this notice board, look for a drive leading to a gate with stone balls on the gateposts. Go up the drive and into the building.

Within the building is a dedication to someone who gave 65 years service. Remove their name from Codeword 1 below to give the next destination – a place in a nearby village:

Codeword 1: CWEAPLIARCWEICANHNISECSMHOITOHLN.

From this place, continue with the narrative below to fill in the Word Grid (page 15) and find the next destination:

Follow the road uphill south west from the main entrance of the building and take the right fork. You will pass a house with several covered lanterns on top of a wall outside. The name of this house is **Clue 1**. Carry on over the brow of the hill and turn left at the T-junction. You will see a religious place (the first name on the date stone above its door is **Clue 2**). Continue until you see a public foot-path signed to the village from which you came. Past this sign is a gravel path passing underneath a tunnel of trees and next to a

Clue 11
Clue 10
Clue 1
Clue 3
Clue 7
Clue 12
Clue 16
Clue 8
Clue 2
Clue 15
Clue 13
Clue 14
Clue 9
Clue 4
Clue 5
Clue 6

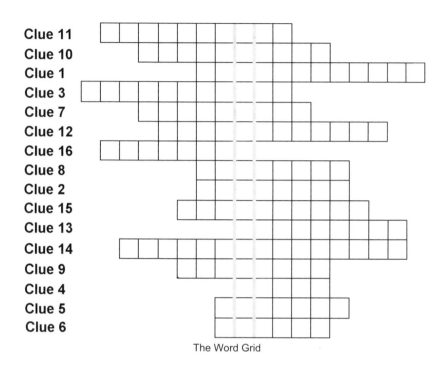

The Word Grid

stream. Follow this path until it turns into a track and emerges onto a main road. Opposite is a building with red letters on the side. The name of the building is **Clue 3**. Turn left onto the road and continue past the village green. Look for a plaque in memory of a school-teacher who died in the winter. Write down the year mentioned as Date 1.

Date 1 _____

Carry on along the road, turning left along another road just before you reach the red phone box. After about 50 yards is a member's club on the right. The last three words of this club make up **Clues 4, 5** and **6** respectively. After this club, turn right up the next road, passing a cottage with a single word name, part of which was a famous Charlton. This is **Clue 7**. Soon after this, **Clue 8** is the house with the PVC stained-glass double doors. Turn right downhill (you've been here before)! Keep following the road around and turn left at the T junction, going uphill and passing a cottage named after a herb (first word is **Clue 9**) and a house with 4 chimney stacks, named, presumably, after one of its own features (**Clue 10**). Further up this road, on the right, is a cottage (first word is **Clue 11**) after which is a garden with a cave in it! The next named house (**Clue 12**), also on the right, could be home to many birds. After this, on the left, is a large house with its name in the bars of the gate (**Clue 13**) and near to this is a house with a date stone above the door (house name is **Clue 14**). Write down the year on this date stone as Date 2.

Date 2 ___

Just before the road signs at the end of the village is a large house with its name on the gate (**Clue 15**). Carry on up the road (do not take the right turn). The next house on the left also has its name on the gate (first word is **Clue 16**).

Completing The Word Grid:

The highlighted column in the grid shows the starting place for the next part of the hunt, which is quite close. Bon voyage!

From the front gate of this place, walk down towards the back of its land past the bench with the "PRIVATE" sign. Follow the gravel (and later grass) path through the narrow gate straight on through the orchard then through the stone stile (and **not** the private gate to its left) and by the side of the stream, eventually over the stone bridge with wooden handrails until you meet the road.

Go left along this road then turn up the next road on the left. Follow this road and take the right fork past a row of white houses. Take the public footpath just after the toilet block on the right. After a short while you will have to cross a couple of small fields. Squeeze through the stone stile at the other side of the second field and take the uphill footpath where the path splits at the sign. When the footpath joins another road, take the road left (uphill), then turn up the next path to the right, passing the house where birds' nests are prominent.

Continue up here until you reach a track adjoining this one. Turn sharp right up this track, going past the house and along the white gravel driveway over the stile and into the woods. The path is narrow and quite obviously not used much. It soon splits into two. You must take the uphill route. After a short but strenuous climb the woodland yields to a steep meadow. Keep going up. When the (fairly faint) path starts to level out and begins to skirt the hill, look uphill and you will see a large tree at the top of the hill. Go towards it. You will see it is not actually at the top of the hill but its trunk rises at the junction of dry stone walls. One of the walls has barbed wire along the top, and growing just in front of this wall are two hawthorn bushes. From the leftmost one of these, count the wooden posts holding up the barbed wire fence in a downhill direction. The number to count is the **primary digit of Date 1 above**. (See page 4 for instructions on how to calculate primary digits.)

The treasure was found by counting paces starting from the foot of the wall next to this fence post downhill directly towards the nearby tree without foliage (is it dead)? The number of paces to count is the **primary digit of Date 2 above**.

The treasure codeword was hidden under a grass sod.

Hunt 3: Eyam

Map: Ordnance Survey Explorer 24 or Outdoor Leisure 24.

Starting point: The Miners' Arms, a famous old pub close to the centre of the historic village of Eyam. The Miners' Arms is at grid reference SK221765.

Terrain: Around 3km walking, 1km of which is off-road. No steep hills, but some sure-footedness will be required at the end of the hunt.

Duration: Around 3 hours.

Solution: page 69

Within the Miner's Arms you will find several items on the walls. From those items you will find two things, as follows:

Look for a story inside the pub detailing an event where someone who should have known better got drunk, then made a costly mistake. You need to find the name of the person **who inspired the misdeed**. This name should be removed from Codeword 1, below.

Codeword 1: HJEOAYHZANEMBLASTRNELOEAWYRCDOOERONNMS

Now look around for a displayed letter, dated Sept 1st. Look on the map for a nearby place named after the writer of this letter, **perhaps implying a state of health**. Write this place down as Destination 1 below.

Destination 1: _____

Go to a nearby building and find the dates that the writer of the letter was in office in service of the village. Use **the primary digit of the year that person started in office** as the "across" co-ordinate (grid position) on the Word Search opposite, and **the primary digit of the year that person finished in office** as the "down" co-ordinate.

Now go to Destination 1 and continue the hunt by following the instructions in the Word Search, initially from left to right, starting from the given co-ordinates. See page 5 for details of how to follow a Word Search.

Carry on from the instructions found in the Word Search as follows: Turn left down the marked public footpath and follow the narrow path until you see a bench and a stile in close proximity to each

	1	2	3	4	5	6	7	8	9	10	11	12	13	14	15	16
1	E	S	—	U	N	T	E	A	⌐	S	E	¬	U	S	N	¬
2	R	T	E	⌐	L	I	R	C	H	O	M	H	O	E	O	T
3	0	—	M	Y	O	U	⌐	Y	—	T	—	J	U	S	⌐	H
4	0	F	¬	N	E	A	R	B	A	—	D	A	N	F	E	E
5	3	O	D	L	E	H	T	—	T	⌐	R	O	C	T	L	⌐
6	L	R	A	⌐	W	O	■	T	U	E	O	I	T	|	T	H
7	T	H	O	R	R	R	I	K	R	H	N	¬	I	W	|	E
8	|	E	—	N	A	G	N	N	N	T	¬	A	T	E	N	M
9	W	.	N	A	M	⌐	R	I	L	U	P	N	H	E	W	T
10	O	|	I	G	N	¬	D	⌐	F	O	⌐	D	L	A	¬	E
11	L	F	S	⌐	H	W	L	A	E	⌐	K	G	—	T	F	B
12	L	O	|	A	T	I	⌐	P	R	U	E	N	R	H	O	|
13	E	—	A	L	B	L	D	I	C	T	E	I	O	T	O	H
14	E	S	E	H	W	U	E	T	—	.	P	O	U	P	A	T
15	U	⌐	N	T	⌐	R	R	U	R	E	L	G	G	H	—	A
16	O	Y	⌐	H	G	I	R	—	N	G	A	L	L	I	V	⌐

The Word Search

other, both of which are dedicated to the same person. Remove that person's name from the remaining letters of Codeword 1 opposite to reveal the next destination, hereafter known as Destination 2.

Destination 2: _____

When you reach Destination 2, you will see a plaque. The next name to look for is found by taking the common surname (call this Surname A) of all the people also mentioned on this plaque.

Surname A _____

Now use Surname A as the **forename** of a person who was romantically linked to someone else according to village folklore. Find the name of this "someone else" by looking on a colourful window within a prominent nearby building. Remove this person's **full name** from Codeword 2 below:

Codeword 2: EDMCRMUOCAKLTCSEYTUCDHALULRCLAH

Go back to Destination 2 and to the road around the back of the property. Carry on up this road past a white sign on the right detailing a historical event until eventually the road stops in a kind of cul-de-sac. Take the track marked as a footpath next to one of the houses into open land. Keep following the track until a stile leads you to a path between fields. Eventually another stile takes you to a path through the grass across an open field. When you reach a prominent rock sunk into the grass you will see nearby a tree-covered grass hillock. From the rock, walk directly towards the highest point in this hillock and keep going in a straight line over the top until you reach a fallen tree and a nearby tree stump.

On the tree stump, there are several carved messages. One of them is the phrase used on the film posters of a 1992 remake of a classic film. Take the single-word name of the **1950s version** of the film (not the 1920s original, which begins with an N) from the remaining letters of Codeword 2 to reveal the final destination. You may have to ask local people for where to find this place.

When you reach this place, walk down the rocky steps to the flat area and look along the left wall as you look down until you see a narrow gap cutting back upwards which you may be able to squeeze up. The treasure codeword was tucked into one of the holes at the far end above head height.

Hunt 4: High Bradfield

Map: Ordnance Survey Explorer 1 or Outdoor Leisure 1.

Starting point: St Nicholas' church, High Bradfield, at grid reference SK267925.

Terrain: Around 1 km of walking, some of which is off-road. No steep hills, but some sure-footedness may be required in places.

Duration: Around 2 hours.

Solution: page 73

Inside the church at the starting grid reference is a plaque commemorating a soldier who lived at Ughill Hall. Above this plaque is a stone tablet commemorating an incident, which occurred in the nineteenth century. The next destination is the place **where this incident originated**.

On the OS map you will see a footpath leading to this next destination from the main road. Follow the footpath towards it until you see an information board showing details of various nearby points of interest. Close to the centre of the board there is information about your next destination, a building named after the builder and which is on a nearby hill. (The building is marked but not actually named on the OS map.)

When you reach this place, stand at the side of this building and look across the water. You will see a prominent dwelling on the other side partially obscured by trees. Make your way there and go inside.

On the walls within you will see several information sheets listing the story of the building's ownership.

The next destination is the stated burial place of the owner who died in 1695. When you reach this next destination, find the war memorial within its grounds, then go 50 metres to the north-west as the crow flies and look for two **very prominent** earth mounds. In front of the lower one you will see a low wall.

The treasure codeword was hidden in a crack close to the conspicuous bright stone in the wall.

Hunt 5: Monsal Head

Map: Ordnance Survey Explorer 24 or Outdoor Leisure 24.

Starting point: The car park at Monsal Head, found at OS grid reference SK185715.

Terrain: Less than 3km walking, little of which is off-road.

Duration: Around 3 hours.

Solution: page 75

To get from the starting point to the next destination you must complete the following logic puzzle and fill in the "Logic Grid" chart on the next page. You should then be able to complete the Answer Grid, also on the next page and – having done so – read off each of the lines as they appear in the grid. One of the answer lines will give an instruction leading to the next destination.

The logic puzzle

Three pubs in a scenic area have unusual pets as attractions to help bring in the customers. Each pub has a different type of pet in differing numbers. Find the pet, the number owned and the location of each pub.

Pub names: "The Village", "3 Furlongs", "One Mile".

Types of pet: Tropical Fish, Parrot, Goat

Number of pets: 1, 2, 10

Locations: Up the Hill, Up the Road, Down the Valley

Clues:

The 10 Tropical Fish were in the 3 Furlongs.

The "One Mile" pub with the Parrot was Up the Road.

"The Village" was Up the Hill.

Solved it? Time to go to the next destination!

Logic Grid

	1	2	10	Up the Hill	Up the Road	Down the Valley	The Village	3 Furlongs	One Mile
Tropical Fish									
Parrot									
Goat									
The Village									
3 Furlongs									
One Mile									
Up the Hill									
Up the Road									
Down the Valley									

Answer Grid

Type of Pet	Number of Pets	Pub Name	Location

At this next destination, you will find a war memorial, which has an unexpected date on it. Write this date down as Date 1, for use later.

Date 1 _____

Opposite is a public phone box. Use the phone number minus the STD code and subtract the "fiddle factor" 675540 to get the grid reference of the next destination.

Phone number:
minus "fiddle factor":   – 675540
Leaves Grid Ref   SK

Before you proceed to the next destination, find a house that perhaps used to charge for passage. Put the name of the house in the Word Grid opposite as **Clue 1**.

At the next destination, start facing the church front door and follow the path to the left. Keep straight on past the war memorial and turn left along the road. You will see a garden gate with a horn on the letterbox. **Clue 2** is the sign on that garden gate; **Clue 3** is the house name. Further along you will see a house with flowers on the sign (**Clue 4**). Turn left when you reach the end of the row of houses, the name of the last house being **Clue 5**. At the T-junction turn left again and look for a house with "ancient cooking" (**Clue 6**), a house named after some animal clothing (**Clue 7**) and another named after part of a carriage (**Clue 8**). Looking further down the road you will see a distinctive edifice, under the roof of which is a date. Write this down below as Date 2.

Date 2 _____

Nearby is a bridge. The name of the bridge is **Clue 9**, and can be found on a nearby plaque.

Now read the highlighted column in the Word Grid (on the next page) to get the next destination, which is quite close by.

Remove the blue writing on the front wall of the destination from Codeword 1 below to reveal the next place to go to:

Codeword 1: ERYOREBAIRNMSSHOASSNOPS

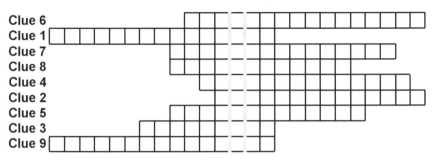

Clue 6
Clue 1
Clue 7
Clue 8
Clue 4
Clue 2
Clue 5
Clue 3
Clue 9

The Word Grid

Inside the lounge of this next place is a photograph of part of a building in a nearby village. (There are several photographs; you have to guess the appropriate one from the context of the next paragraph.)

The final part of the hunt starts from the path passing this "part of a building". Go around the path until you see a door with a sundial above. At this point walk along the path leading away from the building, looking for a face on one of the stones on the right side of the path.

Calculate the **primary digit of Date 2** and count this number of these stones along the path uphill.

Then calculate the **primary digit of Date 1** and, starting from the stone opposite, count this number of stones in the same direction.

On this stone you should be able to find the details of dates and final ages of an 18th-century local family. The treasure codeword was placed fairly close to here.

Hunt 6: Hathersage

Map: Ordnance Survey Explorer 1 and 24 or Outdoor Leisure 1 and 24.

Starting point: St Michael's church, Hathersage, found at OS grid reference SK234819.

Terrain: Less than 2km walking, 1km of which is off-road.

Duration: Around 2 hours.

Solution: page 79

As the hunt proceeds, you will find the answer to the clues, which are to be crossed off the Word Finder Square opposite.

Within the church, find the **first name** of the famous man who sat on one of the ornate chairs (remove the name from the Word Finder Square), then the name of the person **who did the bookbinding on the memorial book** (also remove from Word Finder Square). Now find the first name of the first recorded Rector of the church, whose surname is not known, and remove it from the Word Finder Square. Now go out of the main door and continue the hunt.

Turn left and follow the downhill path. Take the **shortened** name dedication on the bench next to the stile from the Word Finder Square, also the common name of the **stone item it faces and the first name of Ada's husband, found nearby**. Carry on down the path through the gate until eventually you reach the road. Turn left along the road, looking for the plaque containing the inscription of the memorial walk (remove the **first name of the walk** from the Word Finder Square).

On the right side of the road is a house whose name is **loosely connected with a well-known grave** at the starting place (remove house name from the Word Finder Square). Look also for the date stone on this house and use this year to get the OS Grid Ref. of the next destination as follows:

Year house was built
multiply by 150   x 150
=
add 2187   + 2187
= OS Ref.   SK

H	F	I	N	J	A	M	E	S	F	U	L	T	O	N	D	S
A	T	H	B	A	E	C	O	T	T	A	G	E	T	H	P	H
L	A	T	R	C	I	S	N	E	A	R	E	N	O	W	H	U
L	N	U	O	K	G	H	T	H	E	N	T	A	I	K	I	T
C	E	O	O	T	J	A	N	A	S	C	O	L	I	T	L	T
O	H	E	M	H	P	A	T	H	T	O	L	T	H	E	I	L
T	R	I	C	O	G	H	T	T	H	I	R	O	U	G	P	E
T	H	T	O	M	B	H	E	S	A	T	I	L	E	F	C	W
A	O	L	T	A	L	I	O	M	W	T	H	E	R	I	E	O
G	H	G	T	S	H	T	L	M	O	S	Z	A	B	B	A	R
E	O	T	A	T	R	A	A	E	C	K	U	N	T	I	S	T
L	O	Y	G	O	R	U	S	E	P	E	T	H	E	T	T	H
R	D	E	E	C	E	W	I	T	H	H	T	H	E	H	W	U
G	L	E	H	C	B	R	O	O	K	H	O	U	S	E	O	R
E	E	I	E	P	E	R	W	H	I	C	H	N	H	O	O	L
D	E	S	T	H	A	L	B	E	R	T	E	T	E	R	D	E
A	S	S	U	R	S	A	X	O	N	C	R	O	S	S	E	Y

The Word Finder Square

Before you proceed to the next destination, there are a few more words to find in the Word Finder Square. Carry on along the road for a short while and take the narrow lane to the right (remove the name of the house **opposite the lane** from the Word Finder Square). Look for the names of an **unusually named house** and a **sweepingly named** cottage (remove both from Word Finder Square). Keep going in a straight line and as you hit the main road you will see another house name to remove from the Word Finder Square.

Now go to the next destination found earlier, find the pub and look within for a painting scene where **the prey appears to have eluded the hunter**. Remove the name of the painting from Codeword 1 below, and to reveal the last destination, remove the **Latin phrase** to be found at the pub from the same codeword.

Codeword 1: SFGORRILNADOLVEISFRTOTRDSUYTASTMIIOONNVRI
CNCIAFNTEGA

Go into the final destination and remove firstly the name of **the installer of the lighting** from the Word Finder Square, secondly the words on the signs banning an everyday item and finally the name of the owner. Now use the remaining text from the Word Finder Square and, starting from outside the building, locate where the treasure codeword was hidden.

Hunt 7: Torside Reservoir

Map: Ordnance Survey Explorer 1 or Outdoor Leisure 1.

Starting point: Torside Information Centre, next to Torside Reservoir and found at OS grid reference SK067983.

Terrain: Mainly driving with less than 2km walking, 1km of which is off-road.

Duration: Around 3 hours.

Solution: page 83

In the car park, look for an information board for the whereabouts of the next destination, which is **directly under the hillside and to the right of Mountain Hare.**

From this next destination, look around until you find a distinctive pillar, then write down the prominent word near the base as the Cipher Codeword for use in finding the treasure later.

Cipher Codeword _____

Then use the writing on the east side of the same pillar together with the following counting key to find Number A below, by means of the Key Counted Hidden Clue method found on page 5 of this book.

Key: 2, U, 7, 6, 1, T, 4, L, 10, 7, 2, K, 6, 3, 1, 1

Number A _____

Then use the last 6 digits from Number A and subtract 744360 to get the OS map reference for the next destination as follows:

        Last 6 digits of Number A:
              subtract 744360:   – 744360
              = OS Ref:.   SE

In this next destination, you will need to walk around a bit until you find the oldest date stone (on a school). Take the primary digit of that date and place it between the digits of the house number of the political club up one of the side roads, to get the bearing of the next destination from here. Use the bearing on your map to find **a man-made feature more than 2km away.**

When you reach this man-made feature, take the number on the plate next to the most southerly "**Lucy**" thereon as Number B:

Number B _____

Now, by using the Codeworded Cipher routine shown on page 7, use the previously discovered Cipher Codeword to decode the final location of the treasure codeword from:

ODJAASFNJAZCDSGWXTJPPJJIWSOZTYGQWE

WYPKAQNGKINGELMRPLZDR

(using Number B as the number required within).

Hunt 8: Cat and Fiddle

Map: Ordnance Survey Explorer 24 or Outdoor Leisure 24.

Starting point: The Cat and Fiddle Inn, on the A537 Buxton – Macclesfield road. The OS grid reference is SK001719.

Terrain: Around 5km walking, over 3km of which is off-road. Some steep hills and there could be mud in places.

Duration: Around 5 hours.

Solution: page 86

Inside the Cat and Fiddle Inn is a painting of a cat playing a fiddle. **Clue 1** in the Word Grid lower down is the name of the song on the music sheet. Now go west along the road, take the first road to the left and keep going until you see a building that has a sign with trees on it.

Look for a sign against a wall supporting the car park. **Clue 2** is the destination labelled by the top sign and **Clue 3** is the one beneath it. The name of the building itself is **Clue 4**.

Turn downhill at the T-junction. Turn first right then, a while later, right again. Continue to a car park when the road reaches some dwellings. Nearby you will find a house with a round window (name of house is **Clue 5**), a building with a weather vane (the alternative

Clue 10
Clue 6
Clue 9
Clue 4
Clue 7
Clue 3
Clue 5
Clue 2
Clue 8
Clue 1

The Word Grid

name of it is **Clue 6**) and around the entrance of that building is something to fit **Clue 7** which is **above Gorse but under Bramble**. Nearby, outside, there is a bench with a philosophical phrase thereon. Write this phrase repeatedly in the Phrase Grid below until it is full. (The letter "Y" is already given – write around it.)

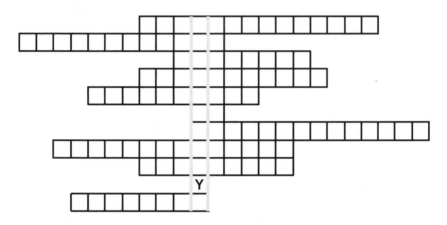

The Phrase Grid

The highlighted column is **label C** on the map at the end of the hunt.

Next go back down the road you came from, and when you reach the T-junction, follow the direction pointing to a single destination (according to the sign). When you reach a parking place on the right get the name of the tree occupied by the red bird (**Clue 8**).

Continue back on the road in the same direction as before, turning left at the next junction and right at the subsequent one. Carry on winding down the road until eventually you reach a pedestrian sign followed by some cottages. Park when you reach the next parking place, which is on the right. Go up the road opposite the parking spot, looking nearby for a notice about **an historic natural event** (the event is **Clue 9**) and, soon after, the name on a gate (**Clue 10**) next to something red which used to belong to it. Now you should have the completed Word Grid overleaf. Read down the highlighted column to get the next destination, which is quite close by.

At the next destination, look in one of the red books near the entrance for a text which you must use in conjunction with the given keys below to discover the following destination and a label for the final map by means of the Key Counted Hidden Clue method. (An example is shown on page 5.) The text to use is **number 600, which can be found on number 528**.

Starting from the beginning of the third line, the counting key to the next destination is:

`10, 2, 5, 7, 7, 5, 4, 5, 9, v, 19`

Also, while you are here and using the same text, find **label F** on the map at the end of the hunt by using the same method but starting from the thirteenth line and with the counting key:

`3, 3, 1, 1, 16, 5, 1, F, 4, 1, 1, F, 4`

At the next destination look around for a place which contains the next three clues as follows:

The first two clues are to be removed from Codeword 1 below and are (in order of removal), a **family motto** and the **name of a shellfish** (both found on the wall).

Codeword 1: DTBEOIHOGEPRAROPTCAKMRORINESESEOMQINRLUEE
AFEIAGDSEETLIS

For Codeword 3, later: take **the name of the island that the plaque with the shellfish depicts.**

The third clue is to locate the next destination and is found by subtracting the **date that "Sir JF" was High Sheriff** from the **date "CF" had his lands restored**. Start the rest of the hunt from the nearest educational establishment found on this bearing.

Year CF had his lands restored
    Year Sir JF was High Sheriff   – _____
Bearing for next destination =   degrees

Starting from the educational establishment you just found, go on to the T-junction, turn left and continue until you reach a **white gate containing the last words to be removed from Codeword 1**. The revealed phrase should show you where to look for the next destination. It should be obvious.

At the next destination you will find both written plaques and graffiti. Use the six-digit birth date (DDMMYY) of someone commemorated here who died in the Second World War. Add the "fiddle factor" 717068 to get the OS grid reference of the final destination, at which point you can use the map at the end of the hunt to locate the treasure.

Date of Birth
Add the fiddle factor   + 717068
= OS Ref   SK

You may have sufficient information to get to the treasure location now, but to make it easier you can find the other labels by following the rest of the instructions below, which can all be found at this location.

To find labels A, B, D and E, use Codewords 2, 3 and 4 below as follows:

Codeword 2: CSJOTAHEPNLSROMLWUELEDNY – firstly, remove **the name which appears twice**, and then the **neatest name** in the graffiti on the top. This will give a concatenation of map **label A** then map **label B**.

Codeword 3: ALALGDAUNENADRNNSDALREAIMPYBSLE – remove firstly the name of the place found earlier on the shellfish plaque and secondly a certain dog's dearest wish for map **label E**.

Codeword 4: RSOTEYAEPLHCULSISAMRSB – remove the name of the commemorated person's regiment to leave **label D**. You should now have all the labels. Proceed to the final destination and good luck!

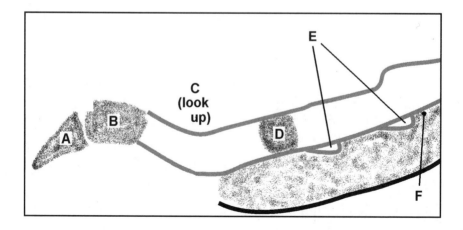

Hunt 9: Edale

Map: Ordnance Survey Explorer 1 or Outdoor Leisure 1.

Starting point: The car park at Edale, OS Grid Ref. SK125853. Pay for the minimum parking time.

Terrain: Around 8km walking, 6km of which is off-road. Please note that this hunt involves some fairly strenuous hill climbing on uneven ground so hiking boots are recommended.

Duration: Around 4 hours.

Solution: page 92

From the starting point, turn right onto the road next to the toilet block and continue for a few hundred yards until you see a black sign with white writing and an arrow. Go into the building indicated and look on a brass plaque for the name of a singing rambler. This is **Clue 1** for the Word Grid overleaf.

Now go outside the building and carry on for a while up the road in the same direction as before. Amongst other things, you will pass a colourful guesthouse sign, a phone box and a pub. Soon you will see a brown diagonally slatted gate with the house name sign above. This is **Clue 2**.

Turn around and go back down the road you came up and you will soon see a house whose name starts with something people use as a head attachment (**Clue 3**). You then reach the pub you passed earlier. Go inside and look for the name of a celebrity photographed at the pub to fit **Clue 4** and the name of two rocks standing in a pool (**Clue 5**). Carry on back down the road and you will soon come across a house name on a rock suggesting fruit picking activity (**Clue 6**).

Further on down the road you will come across an establishment with colourful windows. Go inside and on one of the windows is a dedication to a former proprietor. His middle name is **Clue 7**. Go back outside and continue in the same direction down the road. Look for the name of a house on the gate close to a very old date stone (**Clue 8**).

The highlighted column in the Word Grid is the next destination.

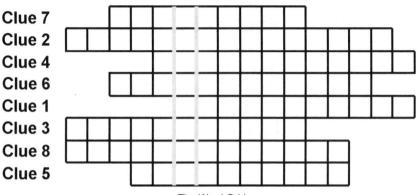

Clue 7
Clue 2
Clue 4
Clue 6
Clue 1
Clue 3
Clue 8
Clue 5

The Word Grid

Reaching this destination, you must take the path to the east, cross the bridge and go through the gate. Here is a sign on which is the name of a plant and of a bird. Remove both these names in the same order from Codeword 1, below:

Codeword 1: RBBEELLDHIREGACTRHHFOEIUERSLDE

The remainder is a name which you will use later.

Now continue along the path towards open country and, when you reach a wall you can use the silhouette clue, below, to locate the next destination. Match the skyline shown to somewhere on the horizon and the arrow will show you where to go for the next destination. (To get the correct scale, the page should be held about 8 inches from your eye.)

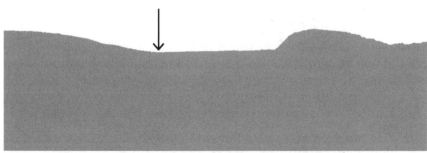

The silhouette

At this next destination you will find a stone edifice with a prominent plaque. It has a person's name on it. Use the person's full name
as the Cipher Codeword to decipher the encryption below by using
the Codeworded Cipher routine described on page 7. It will lead you
to a specific object.

DMFFGIYSUDVHRAJOBDQA

When you reach the specific object, which has many inscriptions
upon it, look for the highest named village upon it, which is the next
destination.

When you get to this next destination you must look for something
bearing the name you revealed earlier from Codeword 1. From this
point follow the tree-covered road around to the east for approximately 200 metres until you reach a road on the left. There is a small
sign pointing up this road with two places marked on it. The final
destination is the top one of the two place names. Go **all the way.**

When you get to the destination, find the path 10 metres to the south
and look for three letters carved into the rock; these are close to a
single letter which looks as though the carver ran out of room at the
first attempt, then completed the graffiti when he found more room
somewhere else.

The treasure codeword was originally hidden under the overhang,
about 10 metres to the left of these carvings.

Hunt 10: Warslow

Map: Ordnance Survey Explorer 24 or Outdoor Leisure 24.

Starting point: The war memorial in Warslow village, OS Grid Ref. SK086586.

Terrain: Around 6km walking, 4km of which is off-road. Please note that this hunt involves some hill climbing on uneven ground so hiking boots are recommended. Also one of the clues may require binoculars or very keen vision.

Duration: Around 3 hours.

Solution: page 96

Fill in the clues in the Word Grid (opposite) as follows:

On the war memorial **Clue 1** is the strangest name, **Clue 2** is a cowboy. You can find the next two destinations by looking in the nearby bus stop area. You will find a plaque describing a prize recently awarded to Warslow. Take the **name of the company which awarded the prize** from Codeword 1 below, then from the remainder take **the name of the prize awarded**. This will leave a concatenation of the next two places to visit, Destination A and Destination B.

Codeword 1: BLBBUEEUTSTTKEECRITPOTNVRGIRLICNLLDAOGENE

Destination A: _____

Destination B: _____

Now go to Destination A and proceed with gathering further clues for the Word Grid.

Find the nearest church in or around this place, look within for the name of **Edward B****'s longer-named daughter (Clue 3)**, then go out of the gate and take the name of the pub **(Clue 4)**. Continue down the road past the public footpath sign on the left. Shortly after is the name of a house with a double garage **(Clue 5)**. Now turn along the road on the left for a short while until you come across a house whose name **could relate to a typical morning meal preference (Clue 6)**. Get back on the main road and continue downhill until you find the name of a large building on the corner next to a narrow path (building name is **Clue 7**). Still following the same road, there is a

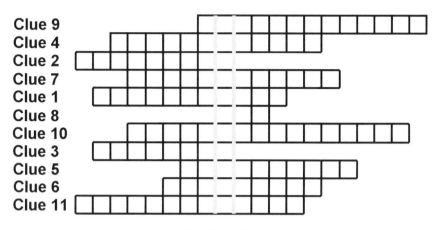

Clue 9
Clue 4
Clue 2
Clue 7
Clue 1
Clue 8
Clue 10
Clue 3
Clue 5
Clue 6
Clue 11

The Word Grid

date stone on a house on the right. **Clue 8** is the 3 letters upon the date stone, **but in alphabetical order. Clue 9** is the name of that house.

Further along, look for the name of a house with a clock on the wall (**Clue 10**). Soon after is a fork in the road. Take the right fork and you will see a house with a small gable over the front door. The name of this house is **Clue 11**.

You should now be able to read down the highlighted column in the word grid to find the specific place within Destination B discovered earlier.

At the specific place you find within Destination B, inspect carefully and you will find a date, which needs to be put into a six-digit number of the form DDMMYY, then take away the "fiddle factor" 60808 to give the grid reference of the next destination:

        Date in DDMMYY form
           Subtract 60808   –   <u>60808</u>
           = OS Ref.   SK

From this grid location, find the pub (which should be very close) and go down the road which has an information board. Soon you will see a house with a coat of arms on one of the outside walls. Take the words on the coat of arms from Codeword 2, overleaf:

Codeword 2: GNRUNTQUAUMFHANLOLRETNTSSIBSCUNARIVREXOW

Now turn down the road running past that wall and find the name of the "underground place" – it has colourful writing – and remove that name from Codeword 2 to give the next destination. Before you go there you will need to get back on the road which has the information board, in the same direction as before, and find the date on the building on the left which is now the black-and-white-signed B&B. Write this date down for use later:

Date 1: _____

Now proceed to the destination found within Codeword 2. Go towards its middle and stop at the point where a path (of sorts) splits away to the right. Then use your binoculars (if you have them) to find two buildings silhouetted against the distant skyline with a large clump of trees appearing between them. (In reality these trees are well behind the buildings.) You may be able to spot them with your naked eyes. These buildings are the final destination. You should be able to locate the buildings on your map.

At this final destination find the footpath passing by the clump of trees that were visible from afar and take the diagonal path away from the buildings towards the corner of a wall. Carry on in the same direction towards two trees that stand on their own. Close by is a wall with a fallen tree lying across it.

Work out the Primary Digit of Date 1 you found earlier, and count this number of standing fence posts to the east from the fallen tree.

The treasure codeword was originally hidden in the wall directly behind that fence post, about a foot above the ground.

Hunt 11: Hathersage

Map: Ordnance Survey Explorer 1 or Outdoor Leisure 1.

Starting point: Hathersage Youth Hostel, found at OS grid reference SK228815.

Terrain: Around 5km walking, 3km of which is off-road. It may be muddy in places if wet.

Duration: Around 2 hours.

Solution: page 100

From the starting point, follow the main road east until you reach **a road "owned by a rock star"**. Turn up this road and keep going until you reach a junction where some guns point the way up the next road. Carry on up this other road for quite a while until a small plaque at a junction refers to a building that used to be here. Take the name of this building away from Codeword 1. The year it started operating is Date 1 below.

`Date 1` _____

Now follow one of the roads from this junction until you find a building linked to something lower down on the plaque. Just before this place, climb over the stile and take the public footpath, which starts on the left side of the road. Go through a field and a gate. Take the two words at the top of the gate from Codeword 1.

Codeword 1: GSTETAEHNRDEGIRNGEWBERAONKRSENCRTHERONOELE

Continue onwards through the woods. At the split in the path, follow the arrow on the stone and look for a sign dedicated to a campaigner. Take the surname down for use later as the Cipher Codeword to decipher the instructions lower down, by means of the Codeworded Cipher routine described on page 7, together with the codewheels on page 8.

`Cipher Codeword` _____

Carry on up the path, over the stile and through the fields. Go through the gate to the left at the buildings and follow the gated path uphill, passing the plum tree. Keep on the path until it reaches a gap in the wall, go through that gap and up the path keeping to the right of the same wall. Now decipher the following using the Codeworded Cipher routine by using the Cipher Codeword you found earlier:

CJLLMGATXTUGPJJIOGBWGUNLAQSEEFELF

This will give you a date, which you must use as Date 2 below to find the grid reference of the final destination, not far from here.

Date 1:

Plus Date 2:   +

plus "fiddle factor" 229162:   + 229162

Leaves OS Grid Ref.   SK

Go to this destination and look around for the item revealed by Codeword 1. The treasure codeword was hidden here.

Hunt 12: Rowarth

Map: Ordnance Survey Explorer 1 or Outdoor Leisure 1.

Starting point: The car park in the village of Rowarth on the western edge of the Peak District, found at OS grid reference SK012892.

Terrain: Around 3km walking, 1km of which is off-road. It may be muddy in places if wet.

Duration: Around 2 hours.

Solution: page 103

In Rowarth, look around the dwellings to find the place names to fill in the numbered clues for the Word Grid overleaf as follows. **Clue 1** is the house with a **reasonable outlook** at a T-junction. **Clue 2** is the cottage whose name **implies a chess player's monarch is no longer in check**. **Clue 3** is the house that **might have been built on a mine**.

While you are still here, use the year on the white date stone on a row of cottages to find the bearing of the following destination, as shown below:

> Year on white date stone:
>> Primary digit of year:
>>> multiply by 50:   X 50
>> Gives a bearing of:

Bearing: _____ degrees

Use this bearing to make it easier to find the named destination from the Word Grid later on by narrowing the area of search on the OS map.

To get the last clue for the Word Grid you must go to **the nearest pub**. **Clue 4** is the surname of the landlord.

While you are in this pub, you must find **the bird's name**, which is to be used later to decipher the last part of the hunt by using the Codeworded Cipher routine shown on pages 7 and 8.

`Bird's name:` _____

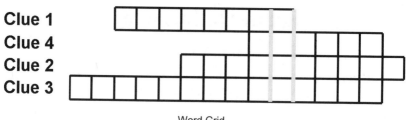

Clue 1
Clue 4
Clue 2
Clue 3

Word Grid

The following destination is a small place (name in the highlighted column of the Word Grid) which you can find on the map at the bearing found earlier.

At the next destination you must find the name of the house which has a date stone showing the date of a great city disaster (remove the house name from Codeword 1 below). Then, carry on along for quite a while on the same road until you reach a sign showing the name of an establishment linked with birds and mammals (remove establishment name from Codeword 1).

Codeword 1: HCSIHCELSOLTOCNBUTOYCTEDTANOTGROEE

Codeword 1 is now revealed to be the star of a recent film.

Go back along the road in the direction you came from and turn down the road on the right. Follow this road for around half a mile, **until you reach the film star just revealed**, at which point you can use the Codeworded Cipher below, together with the bird's name you found earlier as the key to finally locate the treasure codeword:

Codeword Cipher:

KAIUWPYVKEPMRTCHKRMKXHVRIIBWVTPURS

GDTRYSBARINCMHEEPEWRSYE

Hunt 13: Hollinsclough

Map: Ordnance Survey Explorer 24 or Outdoor Leisure 24.

Starting point: Hollinsclough village, found at OS grid reference SK065665.

Terrain: Around 4km walking, 2km of which is off-road. It may be muddy in places if wet.

Duration: Around 3 hours.

Solution: page 106

Look around the starting point for the date of the building with the bell tower (use the year as **Date 1**), and another earlier date stone (use the year as **Date 2**). Add the two dates to a "fiddle factor" of 88030 to find the grid reference of the next location as follows:

Date 1:

Date 2:   +

Add the fiddle factor: + 088030

= OS Grid Ref: SK

From this next location, look around until you see some clues to be removed from Codeword 1, below:

Codeword 1: HGESLNUORTTYFOBTENRWRGIROSAFRNODRGSDE

Firstly you need to remove the name of the Prince, which is carved in marble on the same side as the person whose surname was the other half of a famous comedy partnership, paired with a chap called Lou.

Secondly you must remove that which, according to a sign in the area, repels anger. This will leave the name of the next destination, which doubles up as **Clue 1** on the Word Grid overleaf.

Before moving on to the next destination, on the same sign you will find two words to fit **Clue 2** in the Word Grid.

When you get to the next destination you must find the year of the main building and **remove the even digit from it** to leave the bearing of the following destination, which is less than 5km away as the crow flies.

Use the map to locate the village at the bearing given, locate the south-facing public place with a fruity name (**Clue 3**) and from here, walk in a westerly direction taking the narrow road to the right of a café that is, **to be blunt, a reddish colour (Clue 4)**. Keep going and pass **Clue 5**, which is a place with a sign containing a silhouetted animal, and a Latin phrase above the door. Keep walking down this road, pass the outhouse on the left and take the left fork, then, coming out onto the road, you will see **Clue 6** to the right, which **might be a place to cure children's toys**.

Following the main road downhill you will pass a house with a flowery name (**Clue 7**). Turn next right and take the road west until you come across an ivy-covered dwelling on the road to the right with its name on the doorknocker (**Clue 8**). When the main road forks, take the smaller road towards the fields and look for a house dated the year the metropolitan police were formed (**Clue 9**). On the wider road to the south is a seasonally named house (**Clue 10**). Get back to "the south-facing public place with a fruity name" where you began this part of the hunt and go eastwards along the main road until you find a house on the left with a wooden name plaque referring to a metallic outlook (**Clue 11**).

Continue until you reach a road on the left. Turn up this road, then

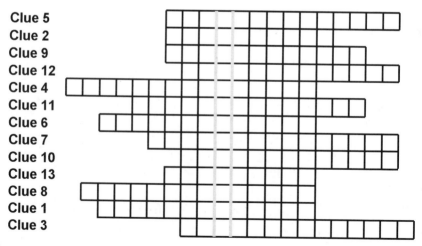

The Word Grid

stay on it and look for the name of a house which may collect silver (**Clue 12**) and another that might not charge for lodging (**Clue 13**).

Now find a nearby information board and, by using the Key Counted Hidden Clue method, (an example is shown on page 5), finish the hunt from the destination shown in the highlighted column of the Word Grid. Start from the first paragraph after the title of the information board. The silhouette shown underneath is part of the clue.

The counting key:

4, 2, 3, 2, 2, 3, 15, L, 11, 5, R, 1, Z, 43, 6, L, 2, W, 19, 1, 23, 4, 26, 5, 16, B, 2, 17, 1, 16, F, 14, 4, 1, 3.

The silhouette

Hunt 14: Curbar Edge

Map: Ordnance Survey Explorer 24 or Outdoor Leisure 24.

Starting point: A parking area on the C road above Curbar, found at OS grid reference SK262747.

Terrain: Around 4km walking, 2km of which is off-road. It may be muddy in places if wet. You may have to pay a small parking fee, depending on how you approach one of the clues.

Duration: Around 3 hours.

Solution: page 110

Look around this area until you find roadside rocks with biblical carvings upon them. Find the rock that shows **seventy-eight minutes from the turn of the day** and remove the word you find from Codeword 1 below.

Codeword 1: IHOESLDBRAOEOKSINSSAAOUCHRE

Using the same word you found as the Cipher Codeword and by means of the Codeworded Cipher routine shown on pages 7 and 8, decode and follow the instructions contained in the Cipher below:

YWDGWGJLOFEFLCRFLXXBOFMTAVRVUGLQLX

IKKBPMB

Go into the place you find and look around until you see an advertised food item on an old, framed photograph under "Pearson's Weekly". Remove this word from Codeword 1, to reveal Location A, to be used later in the hunt.

Location A: _____

From here onwards, find clues to fill in the Word Grid (opposite page).

From your current location, go east and take the left turn at the next roundabout. After another 200m or so you should take the name of the first house (**Clue 1**) on a road going to the left **characterised by a large reference to a former Coronation Street character**. Further on, as the road curves around to the right, there is a cottage with an owl on the name sign (**Clue 2**). Soon after this take the road to the left. You will come to a meeting of several roads, where you can find a house with a couple of round windows (**Clue 3**). Keep on the same road until you see a house name (on the gates) related to water (**Clue 4**). Further on is a large dwelling with a gravel drive (**Clue 5**) and another built when the Prince Regent reigned as monarch (**Clue 6**). If you now double back, then go along the small road to the left you will see the name of a house where someone who is neither a carnivore nor an omnivore now lives (name of house is **Clue 7**).

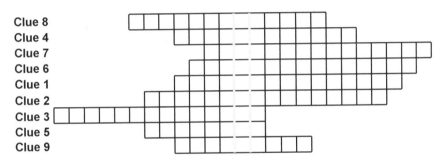

Clue 8
Clue 4
Clue 7
Clue 6
Clue 1
Clue 2
Clue 3
Clue 5
Clue 9

The Word Grid

Carry on down the road you came up until you reach the green with two metal benches, and turn left. Follow the road until you see the house with the tree-lined drive (name is **Clue 8**). Further on is a house with a reference to cooking with eggs (**Clue 9**).

Now go to Location A, find the church and find the name of the person buried here who became more famous by association several years after she died! This clue can be found around the church entrance. Remove the name from Codeword 2 below to leave another name to use later (It is used in the Key Counted Hidden Clue as 'NAME' on the next page.)

Codeword 2: JKAITHLEMBENCOAVYAENCDIKSH

NAME: _____

Use the name on the highlighted column in the Word Grid to find the gravestone from which you must take the **date next to the longest name**. (Hint: there is an easy way to locate this gravestone from inside the church.) When you find the date, put it into DDMMYY format to give a six-digit number and add the "fiddle factor" 211036 to get the OS grid reference for the next destination as follows:

Date in DDMMYY format:
plus "fiddle factor":   + 211036
= OS Grid Ref: SK

At this next destination, find the pub and use the information board within, **relating to an inverted image of a bygone day**, and starting from the beginning of the first line proper, use the Key Counted Hidden Clue method (an example is shown on page 5), with the following counting key and the 'NAME' that you found on the previous page to complete the hunt:

20, 8, 46, 5, 1, 1, 1, 1, 3, 1, G, 12, 12, 24, 4, I, 25, B, 5, 31, 7, 1, F, 19, 10, N, 8, 38, 2

The treasure codeword was originally hidden in a crack in the base of one of the two large trees behind the object located within the decoded text.

Hunt 15: Goyt Valley

Map: Ordnance Survey Explorer 24 or Outdoor Leisure 24.

Starting point: Goyt's Lane to the east of Errwood reservoir, at the OS grid reference SK029753.

Terrain: Around 4km walking, 2km of which is off-road. It may be muddy in places if wet. You may have to pay a small parking fee, depending on how you approach one of the clues.

Duration: Around 3 hours.

Solution: page 114

Throughout this hunt you will be asked to find Treasure Location Dates. These are all years and are used at the end of the hunt to pace out the exact location where the treasure codeword was hidden.

From the given starting point, look around until you find a prominent feature on the wall of the road you are on. Then remove one of the Latin phrases therein from Codeword 1 below:

Codeword 1: GCRAATTTIAACHPRXELATEULNRANS

From this point, take the road west past a **green door of convenience** and keep going on until you reach a building with 4 windows behind a barrier. Nearby is a post box labelled with the last two words to remove from Codeword 1 to give the next destination.

When you get to this next destination, find the gravel road with "a bell" at the end of it – the words on "the bell" are **Clue 1** in the Word Grid, overleaf. Then find the prominent local building with an information board. On this board are references to a **tasteful** local character whom the Queen Mother commented about shortly before her death. The stated year he deceased is Treasure Location Date 1.

Treasure Location Date 1: _____

Finally, look around the outside of this building for a dedication to someone who provided many years of service. Use the dedication to work out how many years service they gave, then calculate a compass bearing of <number of years service> x 7.5 as follows:

Last year of service:
first year of service: –   _____
years of service:
multiply by 7.5:   X   7.5
= bearing:

Now look on the OS map for the next destination – the closest church you find **on this approximate bearing**.

From this destination, look for the other clues to fill in the Word Grid as follows:

Look around for **the house with "blank doors"** and use the date it was rebuilt as Treasure Location Date 2.

Treasure Location Date 2   _____

Then follow the road in a westerly direction until you see a modern house on a corner. Use the date on its date stone as Treasure Location Date 3.

Treasure Location Date 3   _____

Use the house name as Word Grid **Clue 2**. Carry on around the corner and look for the black name sign (**Clue 3**) of a house **which could be a refuge for a certain type of tree**. When you reach the road junction, you will see a house built when the British Prime Minister was Robert Banks Jenkinson. The house name is **Clue 4**. Go down the road immediately across the junction and turn right. Look for a wall with a house name (**Clue 5**) built into it. Now double back and follow the lane over a bridge then take the left fork. Soon you will see

Clue 4
Clue 7
Clue 8
Clue 1
Clue 3
Clue 6
Clue 2
Clue 5

The Word Grid

a house with a wooden sign showing a house name relating to financial matters (**Clue 6**). After this, **Clue 7** is the name of the house **after** the old school. Double back again and take the steps downhill to the right then turn left at the road. Keep going and you will pass a literary building on the right with a date stone. Use the year upon it as Treasure Location Date 4.

Treasure Location Date 4 _____

Carry on along this road until eventually you will see a house with an old-style lamp above the door. The name of this is **Clue 8**.

You should now be able to read the next destination in the highlighted column. This is to the south and is marked on the OS map. Go there then follow the road again in a westerly direction until you find a building sheltered by trees. Look for the date stone above the door and across the road from here you will see a footpath sign with a dedication to a Canadian person. At the top of this sign are two numbers. Use the first number to calculate the mileage required to reach your next destination by subtracting 132 and dividing the result by 10 as follows:

> First number on sign:
> subtract 132: $-$ ___132___
> $=$
> divide by 10 = mileage: _____

You now have the exact distance to be travelled **starting off in the direction of the date stone, when looking towards it from this sign**. The road curves in various directions, but keep going without turning off for the required distance at which point you should be able to park. Now look in this area for a sign with what appears to be an extended bit on one side. Within the extended part is a small map. Your final destination is the **largest black area** on that map.

When you get to this location, you have another task before you can locate the treasure: Look on the explanatory plaque close by to find the date given in relation to a Coal Mine, to be used as Treasure Location Date 5.

Treasure Location Date 5 _____

Also on the plaque is some information about a shrine. Use the date that the shrine was built as Treasure Location Date 6.

Treasure Location Date 6. _____

Finally, stand underneath the **middle one of three in a row** and facing inwards, count out metres as follows (you can use adult paces):

Forwards <primary digit of Treasure Location Date 4 > paces,

turn left and count <primary digit of Treasure Location Date 1> paces,

turn left again and count <primary digit of Treasure Location Date 5> paces,

turn right and count <primary digit of Treasure Location Date 3> paces,

turn right again and count <primary digit of Treasure Location Date 6> paces,

turn left and count <primary digit of Treasure Location Date 2> paces.

You should reach a particular spot at one side of the location. This is where the treasure codeword was originally placed.

Hunt 16: Peak Forest

Maps: Ordnance Survey Explorer 1 and 24 or Outdoor Leisure 1 and 24.

Starting point: Charles King and Martyr church at Peak Forest, found at OS grid reference **SK114792**.

Terrain: Around 5km walking, little of which is off-road. Some steep roads to climb.

Duration: Around 4 hours.

Solution: page 119

Look around the churchyard for the name of a recently planted tree propagated from another. Take the name of the tree you find from Codeword 1, below.

Codeword 1: QMUVIAMLWLDEINALONERCLITMATDUAHMBOERYINLE ACNULLAWA

Now use the date this tree was planted as a six-digit number of the form DDMMYY and add the "fiddle factor" 54512 to this number to get the OS grid reference for the next destination as follows:

> Date in DDMMYY format:
> plus "fiddle factor": + 54512
> gives OS Grid Ref. SK

Go to this grid reference and proceed to fill in the Word Grid (overleaf) with clues found there.

Find the red phone box and take the road uphill. Near to a blue sign you will see a building with 4 columns supporting a balcony. The **highest** date thereon is Date 1, below:

Date 1 _____

Carry on uphill and take the path to the left past a memorial bench and when you reach the road, continue to the left firstly passing a house named after a group of pedigree dogs, (the house name is **Clue 1** in the Word Grid), and then a house name possibly referring to drab monks (**Clue 2**)? Double back on the road and, keeping to the left, follow the steep path with the handrail uphill. Keep to the left and soon you will pass an old house with 2 chimney stacks and an

Clue 11
Clue 1
Clue 10
Clue 5
Clue 6
Clue 8
Clue 4
Clue 9
Clue 2
Clue 7
Clue 3

The Word Grid

unusual old rock name plate (house name is **Clue 3**). Pass to the left of the house and carry on. You will soon see a house with a circular name stone – the house **after** it is **Clue 4**. Carry on along the road until you eventually pass a house **whose name suggests a decent outlook over the dale** (the house name – **Clue 5** – is underneath a face). Keep going uphill until you eventually reach a crossroads. Turn right and look for the house named after a coloured drink of olden days (**Clue 6**). Turn right down the next road and walk on until you find a house with a colourful name sign and a wooden lattice around the door (house name is **Clue 7**).

Now look nearby for Date 2, which is the year on a building linked with a youth movement.

Date 2 _____

Keep going until you pass a house which has an unusual chimney pot, and is covered with a creeping plant (**Clue 8**). Turn left when the road reaches a T-junction and take the later of the two Victorian dates from the chapel as Date 3 below:

Date 3 _____

Carry on until you see a house name (**Clue 9**) at the entrance to a long drive on the left. Now double back along the road and carry on until the road ends at another T-junction where you will see a large white building (name is **Clue 10**, year on the date stone is Date 4, below):

Date 4 _____

To finish the Word Grid, turn down the road. **Clue 11** is the name of the house that could have been named after a cat.

Now, by reading down the highlighted column in the Word Grid you should find the next place to go. When you get there, use Dates 1-4 you have already found to find the point at which you should start reading the Word Search, below, as follows:

Number to start (across) = **Primary digit of Date 1 + Primary digit of Date 2**.

Number to start (down) = **Primary digit of Date 3 + Primary digit of Date 4**.

The Word Search – see the example on page 5 – is shown below. This

	1	2	3	4	5	6	7	8	9	10	11	12	13	14	15	16
1	E	⌐	N	S	E	M	O	R	L	—	A	N	F	I	N	D
2	H	M	A	L	M	I	M	I	A	⌐	A	D	⌐	W	⌐	|
3	T	⌐	O	C	L	L	D	N	I	W	L	H	T	I	N	T
4	O	N	D	L	E	H	T	—	M	O	R	F	⌐	■	E	H
5	L	D	E	⌐	T	I	D	O	N	—	T	H	R	O	D	E
6	M	E	W	D	H	S	E	L	E	S	A	E	⌐	O	R	|
7	A	N	O	R	E	N	L	A	N	D	R	H	C	D	A	G
8	E	⌐	L	L	N	I	O	O	L	⌐	H	U	H	⌐	R	E
9	G	A	L	I	|	|	K	⌐	N	—	P	R	C	V	O	M
10	■	E	—	V	G	O	O	F	I	T	A	L	⌐	E	⌐	W
11	T	H	N	E	N	A	R	I	F	M	E	M	E	|	F	A
12	L	O	T	M	D	M	|	W	E	⌐	R	O	H	T	L	Y
13	⌐	T	.	N	T	M	M	L	D	N	I	S	—	H	A	|
14	O	G	⌐	E	H	O	A	N	—	A	A	L	⌐	N	E	B
15	H	E	—	T	L	C	E	Y	P	⌐	R	O	T	H	E	E
16	T	—	D	N	A	—	R	A	R	S	D	L	—	E	W	T

The Word Search

will lead you to a specific house. Remove the name of this house from Codeword 1 to leave the next destination.

At the next destination, look for a metal plaque on a rock which celebrates an 18th-century pioneer. Using the wording of the main narrative on the plaque and by means of the Key Counted Hidden Clue routine, an example of which is shown on page 5, decipher the following, which will produce Date 5:

Find the building 8, 1, 2, i, 11, 1, o, 2, 4, 1, o, 9, 5, 21, 1, w, 1, 7, 28, 3, 14, 1, 2, r, u, b, 7, 5, 25, 5, 4, k, 13, 11, h, 1, 7, 12, 2, 2, o, 1, 4, h, 4, s, m, 3, 1, 5, s, 5, 7, u, 1, t, 5, 10, 1, 2, 2, f, 4, c, 4, s.

Date 5 _____

Now find the centre of the next village from here as the crow flies on a bearing of approximately **15 x the primary digit of Date 5**.

When you get to the next village, find the Saxon Cross. Nearby is a bench with a dedication by someone with a very unusual nickname. The treasure codeword was hidden in this vicinity.

SOLUTIONS

Winster Market House

Solution I: Winster

Winster Market House is located on the main road from west to east through Winster, the B5057, at grid reference SK242606.

Clue 1 – **ROSELEA COTTAGE** is where you can read the leaves.

Clue 2 – **STANFREE HOUSE** (anagram of 'sent fear').

Clue 3 – **EAST BANK** was the name of the road.

Clue 4 – **MARMALADE** cottage.

Clue 5 – **HONEYSPOT** cottage.

Clue 6 – **HAMSTER** cottage.

Clue 7 – **ORCHARD MINE** cottage has the animal skulls.

Clue 8 – **ROWAN** cottage.

The highlighted solution to the grid is **ELTON YHA**. Elton Youth Hostel is on the B5057, around 2km west of Winster. The date stone is above the entrance door and reads **1668**.

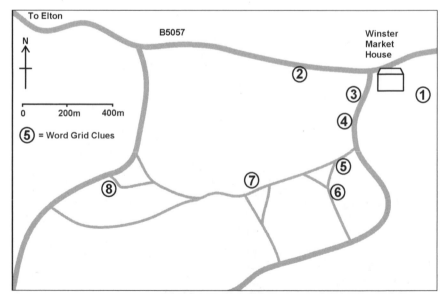

The route through Winster

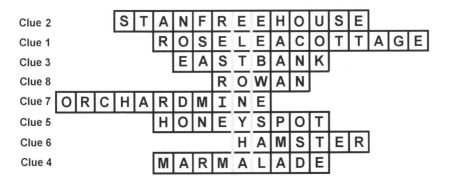

Clue 2		S	T	A	N	F	R	E	E	H	O	U	S	E

The completed solution to the Word Grid

Year on date stone:	1668
Multiply by 100:	166800
Add 44843:	+ 44843
Leaves Grid Ref	**SK211643**

This grid reference takes the hunt to **YOULGREAVE** village square.

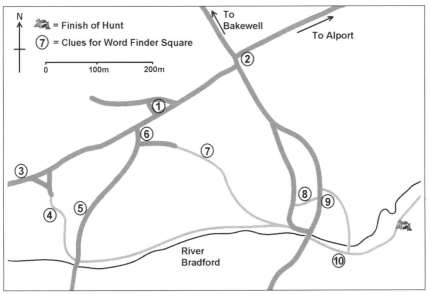

The locations of the clues within the village of Youlgreave

The clues found in the Word Finder Square are as follows:

1. CONDUIT HEAD, THIMBLE HALL

2. ALL SAINTS – "where the high time started in 1870" – the clock, high up on the church tower, is dated 1870.

The other clue here was **THOU SHALT NOT KILL.** (From the Ten Commandments in the south-east entrance to the church.)

Date 1 (on the war memorial) is 1995.

3. PRIMITIVE Methodist Chapel – dated 1895

4. BANK SIDE.

5. TEAS WITH HOVIS (sign at outdoor café "Teas with Hovis – The Rule of the Road").

6. WESLEYAN REFORM Chapel (dated 1857. 18:57 is 3 minutes to 7 – "327"). **BROOKLETON** (name of the road).

7. HUMAN LEAGUE (Had a song "Together in Electric Dreams. Bench says "Sleep Tight Forever in Electric Dreams").

8. ROCK HAVEN.

9. WOODSIDE VIEW (Stone

Thimble Hall

The Methodist Chapel

Electric dreams ...

letter box is on the corner). **BRAEMAR** House is the Caledonian place.

10. CROOKED STICK (The bench which should never get rained on is under a rock overhang.)

The Word Finder Square with the discovered words crossed out:

W	A	F	T	C	R	O	O	K	E	D	S	T	I	C	K
O	E	R	A	T	I	G	H	T	U	B	E	H	N	D	T
O	W	E	S	L	E	Y	A	N	R	E	F	O	R	M	E
D	B	I	N	T	H	E	R	I	U	V	E	U	R	I	A
S	A	S	A	S	B	M	A	G	L	L	W	S	O	L	S
I	N	O	D	E	B	R	A	E	M	A	R	H	L	N	W
D	K	W	R	E	I	E	O	R	C	L	O	A	S	E	I
E	S	B	Y	O	L	I	S	O	A	T	H	L	E	N	T
V	I	F	O	N	C	O	C	T	K	E	C	T	L	I	H
I	D	F	A	F	T	K	H	O	L	L	E	N	T	R	H
E	E	M	E	A	S	U	H	B	N	R	E	O	E	W	O
W	U	A	S	H	I	D	M	A	D	D	E	T	N	I	V
H	N	P	R	I	M	I	T	I	V	E	U	K	O	T	I
H	E	R	O	O	H	E	A	D	T	E	S	I	O	N	S
F	A	T	R	T	E	E	G	R	O	W	N	L	T	I	N
G	O	A	L	L	S	A	I	N	T	S	N	L	I	T	X

This reads "**AFTER A TIGHT UBEND IN THE RIVER IS A SMALL WOODEN WEIR CLOSE BY IS A TEN FOOT CLIFF THE TREASURE WAS HIDDEN IN THE ROOTS OF A TREE GROWING ON IT X**".

This explains where the treasure codeword was found. X was just a dummy letter to complete the Word Finder Square.

Solution 2: Tissington

The map shows the progress of the hunt within the picturesque village of Tissington, clues numbered in the order they are found:

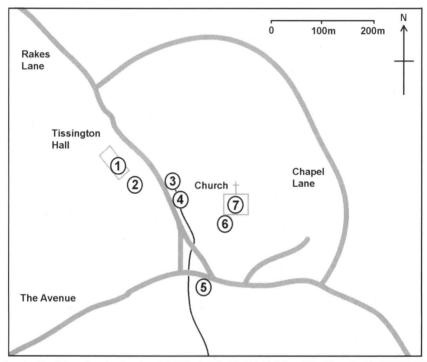

Reproduced from Ordnance Survey based mapping on behalf of The Controller of Her Majesty's Stationery Office © Crown Copyright 2004 100032058

"Within spitting distance of Tissington Hall, (This is location **(1)** on the map.)

Look for a weather vane atop a gold ball **(2)**.

Now look for a well that's shallow and wide **(3)**

And follow the stream which flows from its side" **(4)**.

(5) locates the village notice board. The name dedicated is **KENNETH IAN UNWIN**.

(6) is the wooden bench within 100 metres of here, dedicated to the same person.

(7) on the map shows the building in question – Tissington church main entrance.

Within the church, and close to the organ there is a plaque in memoriam of **ALICE ANNIE SMITH** – the name of the person "who gave 65 years service". Taking this name from Codeword 1 leaves **CWEPARWICHSCHOOLN**. (The extra letters are nonsensical dummies to help disguise the answer.) Proceed to **PARWICH SCHOOL**. Parwich is around 2km north-east of Tissington.

The map below shows Parwich and the route of the hunt. The circled numbers in the map show the location of the matching clues in the Word Grid on page 67.

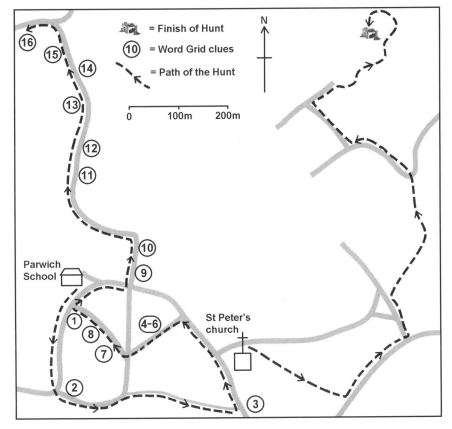

Parwich School is the starting point for the second part of the treasure hunt. It is a converted church, built in 1861.

The answers are:

Clue1 – **LILAC COTTAGE**

Clue 2 – **WESLEYAN** Methodist Chapel

Clue 3 – **SYCAMORE INN**

The schoolteacher plaque is inside the bus shelter and shows the year 1911.

Clues 4, 5 & 6 – **ROYAL BRITISH LEGION.**

The Royal British Legion

Clue 7 – **COSHESTON** (The famous Charlton being Charlton Heston)

Clue 8 – **THE MOUNT**

Clue 9 – **ROSEMARY** Cottage

Clue 10 – **GREEN GATES**

Clue 11 – **WHEATSHEAF** Cottage

Clue 12 – **ROOKERY HOUSE**

Clue 13 – **POOL CROFT**

Clue 14 – **TRUNCLIFFE HOUSE**

The date stone says "MF Mason 1814". So Date 2 is **1814**.

Clue 15 – **SLATE HOUSE**

Clue 16 – **TOWNHEAD**

The correct answers to the word grid are filled in below:

Clue														
Clue 11	W	H	E	A	T	S	H	E	A	F				
Clue 10		G	R	E	E	N	G	A	T	E	S			
Clue 1			L	I	L	A	C	C	O	T	T	A	G	E
Clue 3	S	Y	C	A	M	O	R	E	I	N	N			
Clue 7		C	O	S	H	E	S	T	O	N				
Clue 12		R	O	O	K	E	R	Y	H	O	U	S	E	
Clue 16	T	O	W	N	H	E	A	D						
Clue 8		T	H	E	M	O	U	N	T					
Clue 2		W	E	S	L	E	Y	A	N					
Clue 15		S	L	A	T	E	H	O	U	S	E			
Clue 13		P	O	O	L	C	R	O	F	T				
Clue 14	T	R	U	N	C	L	I	F	F	E	H	O	U	S	E
Clue 9		R	O	S	E	M	A	R	Y					
Clue 4		R	O	Y	A	L								
Clue 5		B	R	I	T	I	S	H						
Clue 6		L	E	G	I	O	N							

The starting point for the last part of the hunt is highlighted within the word grid. This is "**EGLISE DE ST PIERRE**", the French nature of this being hinted at by the "Bon Voyage" message at the end of that part of the narrative. The translation to English is Parwich's own St Peter's church.

From this point onwards the hunt is solved by following the remaining descriptive narrative along the dotted line leading from St Peter's church in the map of Parwich on page 65.

The last part of the hunt involved using the two discovered dates. The number of fence posts to count from the hawthorn bushes is the

St Peter's church

primary digit of Date 1. Date 1 is 1911, 1+9+1+1 = 12, and 1+2 = **3**, so you must count **3 fence posts.**

The number of paces from the wall is the primary digit of Date 2. Date 2 is 1814, 1+8+1+4 = 14. 1+4 = **5**, so you must count **5 paces from the wall**.

The map alongside shows the final location of the treasure:

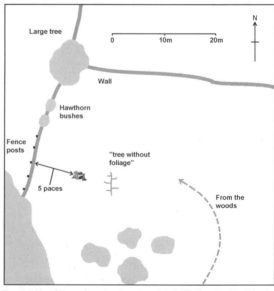

Solution 3: Eyam

Inside the Miner's Arms:

JOHN BARLEYCORN "inspired" the misdeed.

MOMPESSON'S WELL is Destination 1, approximately 1km along the road north from the village hall. (William Mompesson wrote the letter.)

William Mompesson was the Rector of Eyam Church, so the church is the "nearby building".

Mompesson's Well

William Mompesson's dates of office were **1664-1671**. This can be found on the board of Rectors at the far side to the entrance of the church.

1664 makes a primary digit of $1+6+6+4 => 17 => 1+7 = $ **8**.

So the "across" co-ordinate is **8**.

1671 makes a primary digit of $1+6+7+1 => 15 => 1+5 = $ **6**.

So the "down" co-ordinate is **6**. The first letter is a T.

The completed Word Search:

```
     1  2  3  4  5  6  7  8  9 10 11 12 13 14 15 16
 1   E  S  U  N  T  E  A     S  E     U  S  N
 2   R  T  E     L  I  R  C  H  O  M  H  O  E  O  T
 3   O     M  Y  O  U     Y  T     J  U  S        H
 4   O  F     N  E  A  R  B  A     D  A  N  F  E  E
 5   3  O  D     E  H  T  T     R  O  C  T  L
 6      R  A     W  O  ▉  T  U  E  O  I  T     T  H
 7   T  H  O  R  R  I  K  R  H  N     I  W     E
 8   I  E     N  A  G  N  N  N  T     A  T  E  N  M
 9   W  .  N  A  M  R  I     U  P  N  H  E  W  T
10   O     I  G  N     D     F  O     D     A     E
11   L  F  S     H  W  L  A  E     K  G     T  F  B
12   L  O     A  T  I     P  R  U  E  N  R  H  O
13   E     A     B  L  D  I  C  T  E  I  O  T  O  H
14   E  S  E  H  W  U  E  T     .  P  O  U  P  A  T
15   U     N  T     R  R  U  R  E     G  G  H     A
16   O  Y     H  G  I  R     N  G  A  L  L  I  V
```

From the X-Y references found, the Word Search begins at 8 across and 6 down and reads:

TURN UP THE ROAD AT THE NEARBY T JUNCTION AND KEEP GOING THROUGH A VILLAGE. TURN RIGHT WHEN YOU SEE A SIGN WITH A BLURRED PICTURE OF A DRINKING MAN. FOLLOW THE NARROW ROAD FOR 300 METRES UNTIL YOU REACH SOME HOUSES ON THE LEFT WITH A FOOTPATH BETWEEN THEM

The road leads up to the west through the tiny village of Highcliffe and on past the Barrel Inn at Bretton, which has the drinking man sign.

Turning right down this road and on to the houses 300 metres later and you will see a public footpath sign.

The bench and stile are both dedicated to **HAZEL SNOWDEN**.

Removing both JOHN BARLEYCORN and HAZEL SNOWDEN from Codeword 1 leaves Destination 2 – **EYAM TEA ROOMS**. This is on the main street close to the starting point of the hunt.

Built in 1630 this building formed part of
The Bold Rodney Inn
which closed in the year 1901
Plague Victims
Hannah Rowland died here 5th Nov. 1665;
members of her family who died in neighbouring
cottages ~

Mary Rowland	died	1st Dec. 1665.
Abell Rowland	died	15th Jan. 1666.
Thomas Rowland	died	13th Feb. 1666.
Ann Rowland	died	20th Aug. 1666

The plaque at Eyam Tea Rooms

The common surname on the plaque is **ROWLAND**.

The prominent nearby building with the colourful windows is, of course, the church and on the famous "plague window" within the church is a reference to the doomed romance of **EMMOT SYDALL** with Rowland Torre.

The white sign on the right marks the Lydgate Graves and the "prominent rock sunk into the grass" is the boundary stone.

The phrase found on the tree stump is **LOVE NEVER DIES**, from the 1992 remake of Bram Stoker's "Dracula".

The 1950s remake was **DRACULA**. (The 1920s original was called "Nosferatu".)

Removing EMMOT SYDALL and DRACULA from Codeword 2 leaves the final destination, **CUCKLET CHURCH**, at the end of some fields on the south side of Eyam. Local people can tell you where to find it. The treasure was placed in one of the caves.

The boundary stone and grassy hillock

The entrance to Cucklet Church

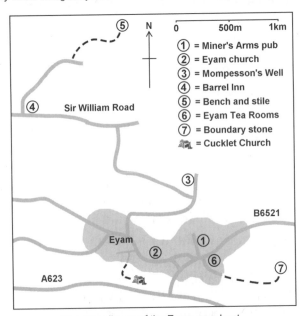

The overall map of the Eyam area hunt

Solution 4: High Bradfield

The plaque you were looking for was on the inside wall of the church on the same side as the door, commemorating Charles Goldthorpe Vickers of Ughill Hall. The stone tablet commemorated the flood of 11th March 1864, which caused many deaths in the Loxley valley of Sheffield. The place it originated was **DALE DIKE EMBANKMENT**. Dale Dike reservoir is marked on the map and the embankment is at grid ref. **SK243917**.

The information board and marker stone

Note the marker stone at the bottom of the foreground tree in the photograph, with the letters CLOB, indicating the **C**entre **L**ine **O**f **B**ank, the location of the original breached embankment.

The information board contains a picture of the next destination, **BOOT'S FOLLY**, an unusual 50ft tower on the hill to the south of Strines Reservoir, named after the builder, Charles Boot. It is simply marked on the OS map as "Tower".

From Boot's Folly you can look across the water and see the "prominent dwelling on the other side partially obscured by trees" – **THE**

STRINES INN. The inn is a 12th-century public house, situated at the head of Strines reservoir, at OS grid ref. SK223906.

The information sheet in question is "**The History of the Strines Inn**". The owner of the Inn who died in 1695 was Anthony Worrall (mentioned on the right-hand panel). His gravestone can be found in **Bradfield Church,** which refers to St Nicholas' church, High Bradfield, the same place the hunt started! This is the next destination.

The war memorial is found at the western end of the churchyard, and 50 metres to the north-west takes you into a wooded area where there is a Motte and Bailey fortification. The latter is said on the information board in the centre of High Bradfield to have been "built by the Normans under William the Conqueror". The lower hill is the Bailey, and in front of this is the low wall with the conspicuous bright stone, close to which the treasure codeword was hidden.

The overall map of the hunt is shown below:

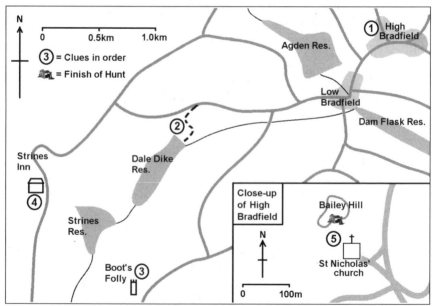

Solution 5: Monsal Head

The logic puzzle grid was filled in as follows:

Logic Grid

	1	2	10	Up the Hill	Up the Road	Down the Valley	The Village	3 Furlongs	One Mile
Tropical Fish	X	X	✓	X	X	✓	X	✓	X
Parrot	✓	X	X	X	✓	X	X	X	✓
Goat	X	✓	X	✓	X	X	✓	X	X
The Village	X	✓	X	✓	X	X			
3 Furlongs	X	X	✓	X	X	✓			
One Mile	✓	X	X	X	✓	X			
Up the Hill	X	✓	X						
Up the Road	✓	X	X						
Down the Valley	X	X	✓						

Therefore, the answer grid reads:

Answer Grid

Type of Pet	Number of Pets	Pub Name	Location
Tropical Fish	10	3 Furlongs	Down the Valley
Parrot	1	One Mile	Up the Road
Goat	2	The Village	Up the Hill

The only answer line that gives an instruction leading to the next destination is "Goat 2 The Village Up the Hill". So you must look around and go to the village up the hill!

The view from Monsal Head up the western valley is towards the next destination, the village of **Cressbrook**, which is "Up the Hill".

Within Cressbrook:

Date 1, the "unexpected date on the war memorial" is **1919** (the First World War ended in 1918 – presumably this date includes those who died as a result of war wounds).

The phone number (minus the STD code) on the red phone box is **871237**.

The next destination is found as follows:

Phone number:	871237
minus "fiddle factor":	− 675540
Leaves Grid Ref	**SK195697**

This grid reference points to the centre of the village of **ASHFORD IN THE WATER**, where the hunt re-commences. The house "which perhaps used to charge for passage" (Clue 1 in the Word Grid) is **THE OLD TOLL HOUSE.**

The war memorial

The map (below) shows where the remaining Word Grid clues are

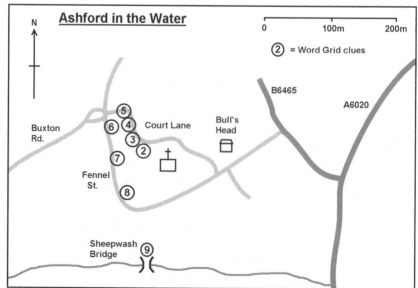

found within Ashford in the Water. (Clue 1 was already found in the previous village.)

Date 2 is under the roof of the pagoda and is **1881**.

Clue																			
Clue 6						O	L	D	B	A	K	E	R	Y	C	O	T	T	A	G	E
Clue 1	T	H	E	O	L	D	T	O	L	L	H	O	U	S	E					
Clue 7						F	O	X	G	L	O	V	E	C	O	T	T	A	G	E
Clue 8						W	H	E	E	L	C	O	T	T	A	G	E			
Clue 4							J	A	S	M	I	N	E	C	O	T	T	A	G	E
Clue 2								T	H	E	W	E	A	V	E	R	S	M	I	L	L
Clue 5						C	O	R	N	E	R	C	O	T	T	A	G	E		
Clue 3					G	R	E	E	N	B	A	N	K							
Clue 9	S	H	E	E	P	W	A	S	H	B	R	I	D	G	E					

The Word Grid solution is shown above and the highlighted column reveals the next destination – "**BULLS HEAD**", a pub in the centre of Ashford.

The blue writing on the front wall of the Bull's Head says **ROBINSONS**. Removing ROBINSONS from Codeword 1 leaves **EYRE ARMS HASSOP**. (The Eyre Arms pub in the nearby village of Hassop, 3km north-east.)

The Eyre Arms

In the lounge of the Eyre Arms, the photograph of a "part of a building in a nearby village" was **THE WEST DOOR OF BAKEWELL CHURCH**.

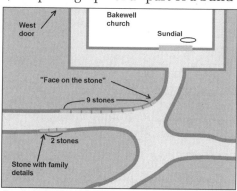

Moving on to Bakewell church, the map alongside shows the remainder of the hunt, starting from the west door. The photograph below shows the "face on the stone" looking towards Bakewell Church (and the door with a sundial above).

Reproduced from Ordnance Survey based mapping on behalf of The Controller of Her Majesty's Stationery Office © Crown Copyright 2004 100032058

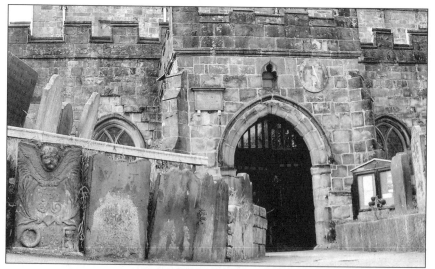

Bakewell church

Date 1 was 1919, Date 2 was 1881.

The first number of stones to count was <primary digit of 1881> = 1+8+8+1 = 18. 1+8 = **9** stones.

The second number of stones to count was <primary digit of 1919> = 1+9+1+9 = 20. 2+0 = **2** stones.

The 18th-century local family was the **GREAVES** family.

Solution 6: Hathersage

The "famous man who sat on one of the ornate chairs within" was **ALBERT**. (Queen Victoria's husband – named on the sign above the chairs as the Prince Consort.)

JAN ASCOLI did the bookbinding on the memorial book. (The credit is given on the front page of the book.) There is a photographic record showing each page of the book.

The first recorded Rector of the church was **WILLIAM**.

The shortened name of the dedication on the bench is **JACK THOMAS**. The common name of the stone item is **SAXON CROSS**, and Ada's husband was **ARCHIE.**

The plaque containing the inscription of the memorial walk is on the wall right next to the path as it joins the road. It is the **SHUTTLEWORTH** memorial walk.

The house "whose name is loosely connected with a well-known grave at the starting place" is **HOOD LEES**. (Little John, Robin Hood ...) Hood Lees was built, according to the date stone, in **1931**.

Year house was built	1931
multiply by 150	x 150
=	289650
add 2187	+ 2187
= OS Ref.	SK 291837

The next destination is at **SK291837**. This is the tiny village of **Ringinglow**.

The house opposite the narrow lane is **HALL COTTAGE**.

The unusually named house is **ZABBAR** and the "sweepingly named" cottage is **BROOM COTTAGE**.

The final named house in the Word Finder Square is **BROOK HOUSE**.

The path of the hunt through Hathersage, from St Michael's church is at the top of the next page.

At Ringinglow, the pub is called the Norfolk Arms. Within the

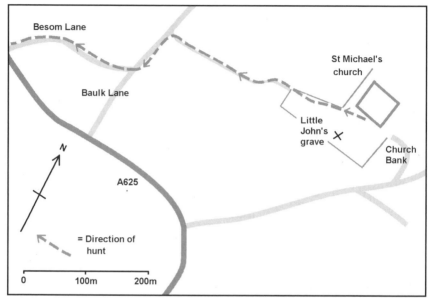

Besom Lane

Baulk Lane

St Michael's
church

Little
John's
grave ✗

Church
Bank

N

A625

= Direction of
hunt

0   100m   200m

lounge of the Norfolk Arms is a painting of a pheasant flying away just as a hunter with a gun passes by. It is entitled "**FROSTY MORNING**".

The Latin phrase is found on the bottom of the pub sign – **SOLA VIRTUS INVICTA**.

Removing FROSTY MORNING then SOLA VIRTUS INVICTA from Codeword 1 leaves the next destination – **GRINDLEFORD STATION CAFE**.

Within Grindleford Station Café there is an old plaque in the main eating area with the name of the lighting installer – **JAMES FULTON**. The sign banning an everyday item is **NO MOBILE PHONES**, and on the wall outside is a wooden plaque giving the name of the owner – **PHILIP C EASTWOOD**.

The remaining words read: "**FIND THE COTTAGE THAT IS NEAR**

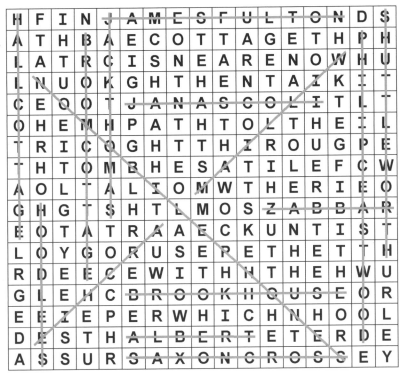

The completed Word Finder Square

Grindleford Station Café – a great place to finish a hunt with a meal and a cup of tea (and ample parking)

ENOUGH THEN TAKE THE PATH TO THE RIGHT THROUGH THE STILE FOLLOW THE RIGHTMOST TRACK UNTIL YOU SEE THE TREE WITH THE HUGE CREEPER WHICH HOLDS THE TREASURE"

The "Y" at the end is just a dummy.

The final section of the hunt, from Grindleford Station café is shown on the map alongside.

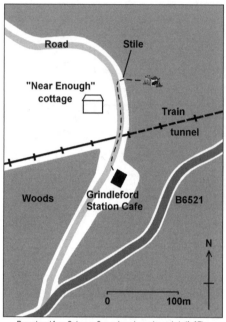

There is a cottage with the name "Near Enough" on the other side of the bridge across the railway track. The path to the right just after it leads to a stile at which the path enters the woods. The path splits, and taking the rightmost path, you will soon come across a distinctive tree with a very large creeping plant right next to the path – the creeper is about half the thickness of the tree. This is where the treasure codeword was originally hidden.

Solution 7: Torside Reservoir

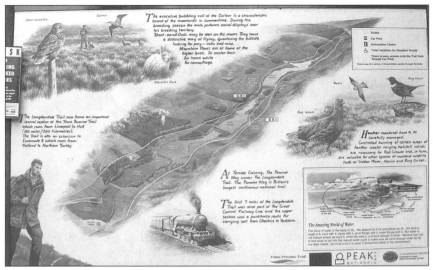

Torside car park information board

The information board showing the next destination is on the southernmost part of the Torside car park and is entitled "Longdendale Trail". The top section has some information about wildlife, and within this section are the words "the hillside" and a titled picture of a Mountain Hare:

The destination "directly under the hillside and to the right of Mountain Hare" is **ST JAMES' CHURCH**, or **WOODHEAD CHAPEL**. This is about 1km to the north-east, on the A628 Woodhead pass.

The "distinctive pillar" at Woodhead Chapel is shown alongside. The prominent word found at the base, to be used as the cipher codeword, is **SLEEPING**.

The writing on the side of the pillar reads "IN LOVING MEMORY OF JOSEPH HIGGINBOTTOM BENNETT OF OWL NEST FARM ...".

When 2, U, 7, 6, 1, T, 4, L, 10, 7, 2, K, 6, 3, 1, 1 are applied to these words using the Key Counted Hidden Clue method shown on page 5, the message **NUMOFTELONEKWEST** appears. The NUM OF TEL ONE K WEST refers to the telephone number of the old style red telephone box, close to Crowden YHA, about 1km to the west.

The number of the telephone is **01457 852419**. Taking the last six digits from this number and subtracting 744360 to get the OS map reference for the next destination gives:

Last 6 digits of Number A	852419
subtract 744360	– 744360
= OS Ref.	SE 108059

This referred to OS grid reference **SE108059**, which is the centre of **HOLME** village, on the northern limit of the Peak District. Go east along the A628 then turn left along the A6024 until you reach Holme village.

Within Holme village, the oldest date stone is found on the main road, above the door of Holme School. The date is **1694**.

The primary digit of 1694 is 1+6+9+4 = 20. 2+0 = **2**.

The political club in question is the Holme Liberal club, and is found at number **15** Meal Hill Road. Putting a "2" between the digits of 15 gives the bearing in question – **125 degrees**. This is roughly south-east.

The man-made feature on this approximate bearing is **WINSCAR DAM**, found just over 5km away. It is shown at the top of the next page, looking from the east.

The "Lucy" in question is an industrial box, the name "Lucy" being stamped on the side. The plate right next to it says "41". Therefore Number B is **41**.

Winscar dam

When the cipher codeword SLEEPING (found earlier at the base of
the pillar in Woodhead Chapel graveyard) is applied to the given
cipher using the Codeword Cipher routine shown on page 5, the
decoded text is revealed as

**GONEPASTBLDGSATCPENTERWOODSDIGTWOPACESNWFROMCORRE
CTPOLE**

In plain English, and with
the appropriate context of
the surroundings, this is
"Go north-east past buildings. At car park enter
woods. Dig two paces
north-west from correct
Pole." (The pole in ques-
tion is a telegraph pole **41**.)

The finish to the hunt is
shown alongside:

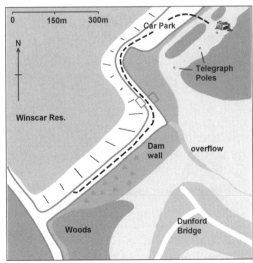

Solution 8: Cat and Fiddle

Clue 1 – the name of the song on the music sheet is **HOME SWEET HOME**.

The building that has a sign with trees on it is the Stanley Arms, about 2km to the west of the Cat and Fiddle.

Clue 2 is **BUXTON**.

Clue 3 is **MACCLESFIELD**.

Clue 4 is the **STANLEY ARMS**.

The next destination "turn down the road at the T-junction and turn first right then a while later right again. Continue to a car park" is the village of Macclesfield Forest.

Clue 5 is **THE SCHOOL HOUSE**.

Clue 6 – "the alternative name of the building with a weather vane" (meaning the church) is **FOREST CHAPEL**.

Forest Chapel

Clue 7 appertains to a list of wild flowers close to the entrance of the church. The only flower in the list which appears "above Gorse but under Bramble" and also fits the spaces for Clue 7 is **FOXGLOVE**.

The phrase on the bench for the Phrase Grid is

**WHAT IS THIS LIFE IF FULL OF CARE
WE HAVE NO TIME TO SIT AND STARE.**

Using this phrase to fill in the Phrase Grid:

Reading the highlighted column, we can see that label C on the final map is **TREE WITH EYE**. The "single destination" on the sign is Wildboarclough – to the right.

In the parking place "the name of the tree occupied by the red bird" refers to an information sign entitled "The Working Forest" which has a picture of a red bird – a Crossbill. The tree (Clue 8) is a **NORWAY SPRUCE**.

The hunt continues on in a southerly direction and the next clue is on the bridge where the T-junction turns left into Wildboarclough. Clue 9 refers to "a notice about an historic natural event", that of a **FLOOD DISAS-TER** on 24th May 1989.

Clue 10 – "the name on the gate" is **THE OLD POST OFFICE**. The "something red that used to belong to it" is the adjacent red telephone box.

Clue 10	T	H	E	O	L	D	P	O	S	T	O	F	F	I	C	E
Clue 6				F	O	R	E	S	T	C	H	A	P	E	L	
Clue 9		F	L	O	O	D	D	I	S	A	S	T	E	R		
Clue 4		S	T	A	N	L	E	Y	A	R	M	S				
Clue 7			F	O	X	G	L	O	V	E						
Clue 3	M	A	C	C	L	E	S	F	I	E	L	D				
Clue 5		T	H	E	S	C	H	O	O	L	H	O	U	S	E	
Clue 2					B	U	X	T	O	N						
Clue 8				N	O	R	W	A	Y	S	P	R	U	C	E	
Clue 1			H	O	M	E	S	W	E	E	T	H	O	M	E	

The completed Word Grid

Reading the highlighted column, the next destination is **ST SAVIOURS**, the church in Wildboarclough.

In St Saviour's church, close to the entrance are the red hymn books. **Hymn 600** is the text in question, and this is found on **page 528**, as hinted at by the clue.

The text from line 3 begins

> I see from far Thy beauteous light,
> Inly I sigh for Thy repose;
> My heart is pain'd nor can it be,

When the numbers given in the hunt are applied, this reveals the next destination: "**ATALLGREAVE**". The "V" was given in the key.

Allgreave is a very small village 2km to the south, consisting of little more than a pub and a Sunday school.

The text from line 13 of hymn 600 begins

> Is there a thing beneath the sun
> That strives with Thee my heart to share?

Applying the other key in the same way gives label F, **TREASATFIVEFT**.

Within Allgreave, the place containing the three clues is the Rose and Crown pub. The family motto can be seen on the descriptive chart about the history of the surname "Fagan", found in one of the back rooms. It is **DEO PATRIESQUE FIDELIS**. Higher up the same chart can be found the answer to the date "Sir JF" (Sir John Fagan) was high Sheriff, **1423**, and the date "CF" (Christopher Fagan) had his lands restored, **1663**.

In the room with the pool table is a map of **ALDERNEY**. This is "the name of the island that the plaque with the shellfish depicts". At the top of this is the name of the shellfish, "The famous **ORMER** – a shellfish found only in the islands". Subtracting 1423 from 1663 gives the bearing of the next destination:

Year CF had his lands restored	1663
Year Sir JF was High Sheriff	– 1423
Bearing for next destination =	240 degrees

The "educational establishment found on this bearing" is Wincle Church of England Primary School.

The words on the white gate in question, slightly south of Wincle village, are "**THE PARSONAGE**".

Removing DEO PATRIESQUE FIDELIS, ORMER and THE PARSON-AGE from Codeword 1 leaves **BIGROCKONEMILEEAST**. The big rock in question is the Hanging Stone, and is approximately one mile to the east. It is marked on the OS map.

Hanging Stone

On the southern face of the Hanging Stone are the plaques from which the required information can be gathered for the rest of the hunt. The person "commemorated here who died in the Second World War" is Lt Col Courtney Brocklehurst of the **ROYAL HUSSARS**. Removing this from Codeword 4 leaves label D as **STEEP CLIMB**.

According to the plaque, he was born on **MAY 27**[th] **1888**, which converts to a six-digit value of 270588.

Date of Birth	270588
Add the fiddle factor	+ 717068
= OS Ref	SK987656

The grid reference is **SK987656**, which is used to locate the final destination containing the treasure codeword, **LUDS CHURCH**. This is a natural open-topped cave and is named on the OS map. The plan view of this cave roughly follows the final map of the hunt.

On the top of the Hanging Stone, the "name which appears twice in graffiti" is **C ALLEN**, and "the neatest name" is **JOHN ROWLEY**. (This name is so neat it looks like it has been done with some sort of template or stencil.) Removing both these names in order from Codeword 2 leaves STEPSMUD.

Label A is therefore **STEPS** and label B is **MUD**.

For Codeword 3, "a certain dog's dearest wish" refers to the plaque about the dog BURKE:

A NOBLE MASTIFF
BLACK AND TAN
FAITHFUL AS WOMAN
BRAVER THAN MAN
A GUN AND A RAMBLE
HIS HEART'S DESIRE
WITH THE FRIEND OF HIS LIFE
THE SWYTHAMLEY SQUIRE

The dearest wish was therefore "**A GUN AND A RAMBLE**". The name of the place found on the shellfish plaque earlier was ALDERNEY, therefore, removing these two in the stated order from Codeword 3 leaves label E – **LANDSLIPS**.

The map of Lud's church, complete with labels, is shown below:

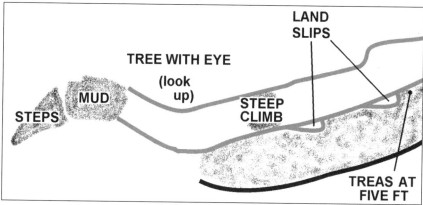

The steps lead downwards from the northern entrance, (which is marked in one of the rocks as "Lud's church"), then you must pass through a pool of mud (which is usually caked solid and has stepping stones), pass a "tree with an eye", which is about 40ft overhead, the "eye" being formed by a branch which appears to make a circle when viewed from below. Then there is a steep climb and the two landslips should be visible on the right.

The treasure was originally placed in one of the cracks in the rock next to the second landslip.

The map of the whole hunt is alongside.

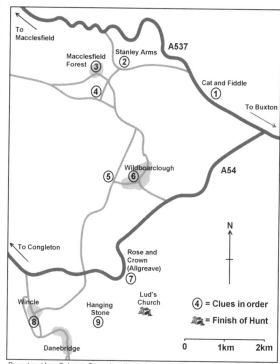

Solution 9: Edale

The building indicated by the "black sign with white writing and an arrow" is Peak National Park Visitor Centre and the plaque in question is about the 1932 Kinder Scout Mass Trespass. The singing rambler named upon it, Clue 1, was **EWAN MACCOLL**.

The house with the brown diagonally slatted gate, Clue 2, is **THE**

The Old Parsonage

OLD PARSONAGE.

The house "whose name starts with something people use as a head attachment", Clue 3, is **WIGLEY HOUSE**. (Wig)

Inside The Old Nag's Head pub are pictures of Mike Harding and **DAVID BELLAMY**, (Clue 4), and the two rocks standing in a pool, Clue 5 – **MOAT STONES**.

The house name on a rock suggesting fruit picking activity is next to the gate of that house, **THE LIME FIELD** (Clue 6).

The establishment with colourful windows is Edale Parish church, and inside, one of the stained glass windows has a dedication to a former proprietor, Francis **BERESFORD** Champion, Clue 7.

The name of the house close to the very old date stone, Clue 8, is **CHURCH COTTAGE**. (The date stone says 1678.)

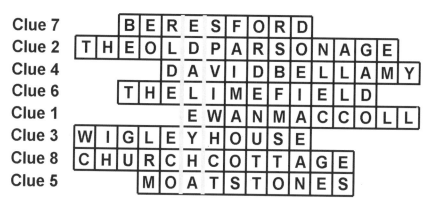

Clue 7   B E R E S F O R D

Clue 2   T H E O L D P A R S O N A G E

Clue 4   D A V I D B E L L A M Y

Clue 6   T H E L I M E F I E L D

Clue 1   E W A N M A C C O L L

Clue 3   W I G L E Y H O U S E

Clue 8   C H U R C H C O T T A G E

Clue 5   M O A T S T O N E S

The completed Word Grid

The highlighted column is the next destination – **EDALE YHA**. As always, this is marked on the map, but it is not in Edale. It is around a mile further down the valley on the slopes of Kinder Scout, close to Lady Booth Brook. You can park outside the Youth Hostel.

On the sign, the name of the plant is **BELL HEATHER**. The name of the bird is **RED GROUSE**. Removing BELL HEATHER then RED GROUSE from Codeword 1 leaves **BIRCHFIELD** – the name to be used later.

The horizon which matches up to the silhouette is shown below, and is the panorama (left to right) of the Lose Hill to Mam Tor ridge:

The next destination, according to the arrow, is named on the map as **HOLLIN'S CROSS**. There are several paths leading up to Hollin's Cross marked on the OS map. If it is not possible to park safely on the road, the nearest place to park will be the Edale car park where you began the hunt.

At Hollin's Cross there is a single stone edifice. The plaque upon it is in memory of **TOM HYETT**. Using TOMHYETT as the Cipher Codeword for the given cipher leaves the decoded message:

WARMEMRLNRHOPECHURCH

The "specific object" is therefore the war memorial near Hope church. This can be found on the left side of the main road towards Hathersage, about 100 metres from the church.

There are four villages, Hope, Thornhill, Aston and Bradwell, together with the commemorated soldiers from each of those villages named on the monument. The village highest named upon the monument is **ASTON**.

Aston is on the lower southern slope of Win Hill. On the

The war memorial

west side of the village, you will find a rock at the end of a driveway showing the name BIRCHFIELD, revealed earlier from Codeword 1. Following the road to the east, you will come across a sign pointing to "WIN HILL & HOPE CROSS".

The final destination, "the top one of the two place names", is therefore **WIN HILL**.

Following this marked path up Win Hill, (a strenuous climb), you will approach the summit from the west. Dropping down to the path 10 metres to the south, you will soon see the three letters in question, together with the first attempt, a single letter just to the left of them, carved into the rock above. The treasure codeword was originally hidden under the overhang to the left. A map of the hunt is shown below:

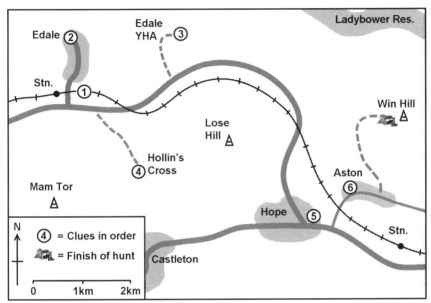

Solution 10: Warslow

Warslow War Memorial is shown below:

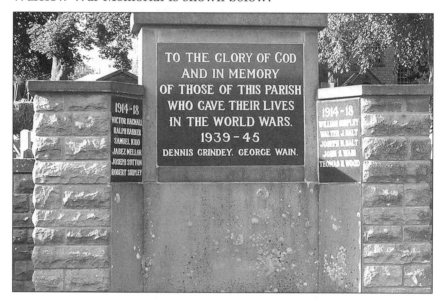

The strangest name (surely), Clue 1, was **JABEZ MELLOR**.

The cowboy, Clue 2, was **JOHN S. WAIN**.

The plaque in the nearby bus stop area describes the award by **BLUE CIRCLE** of the **BEST KEPT VILLAGE** to Warslow from 1995-1997. Removing these words from Codeword 1 leaves BUTTERTONGRINDON. Destination A is **BUTTERTON** and Destination B is **GRINDON**.

On the window of the church at Butterton is a memorial to Edward Birch. The two daughters mentioned are Margaret and Marice. **MARGARET** is therefore Clue 3, the longer named daughter.

Clue 4, the name of the pub, is **BLACK LION INN**.

The house with the double garage, Clue 5, is **BOOTH HOUSE**.

The house "whose name could relate to a typical morning meal preference", Clue 6, is **SUNNYSIDE** (think 'eggs').

The large building on the corner next to a narrow path, Clue 7, is **THE OLD SCHOOL.**

The letters upon the date stone, in alphabetical order, (Clue 8), are **EHJ**, and the date stone is on **BROOKS COTTAGE** (Clue 9).

Soon you will approach the cottages where the road fords the river. The house with a clock on the wall (Clue 10) is **BROOKSIDE COTTAGE**.

The house with a small gable over the front door (Clue 11) is **RIVER-SIDE VIEW**.

The highlighted column within the Word Grid reveals the specific destination within Destination B (Grindon) to be **RINDLE STONE**.

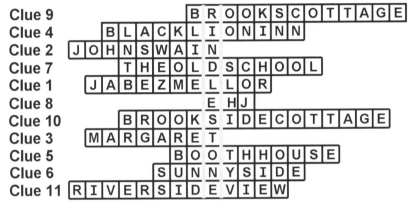

The completed Word Grid

This is a stone column whose purpose was to state the lord of the manor's claim to the rindle (a small stream which only flows on occasion). It can be found close to the entrance of the church.

The date on the Rindle Stone is **17th March 1862,** which becomes 170362 when put into six digits.

Date in DDMMYY form		170362
Subtract 60808	−	60808
= OS Ref.		SK109554

So the grid reference of the next destination is **SK109554**, which is the centre of **WETTON** village, around 3km east of Grindon, on the other side of the Manifold valley.

The house with the coat of arms is High Withins, and the coat of arms says "**NUNQUAM FALLENTIS NIX**".

The "underground place with colourful writing" is **GRUNT'S BURROW**. Taking away NUNQUAM FALLENTIS NIX and GRUNTS BURROW from Codeword 2 leaves **THORS CAVE,** the next destination.

The date on the black and white signed B&B (Date 1) is **1870**.

Thor's Cave is spectacularly placed high up in Thor's cliff overlooking the Manifold valley around 1km to the west of Wetton and is reached by a footpath starting from the western side of the village. It is mentioned on the information board found earlier.

The path (of sorts) which leads up into Thor's cave splits away to the right, leading to an aperture in the western side of the cave. At the point of the split in the path, the target destination is framed by the opening of the cave.

The buildings silhouetted against the skyline shown above are those of **SUMMERHILL FARM**, over 2km to the north. A good place to park is at Wetton Mill, in the Manifold valley, which gives a pleasant walk up past "the Sugarloaf", an unusually shaped hillock on the way to Summerhill Farm.

The view from the centre of the cave to the north showing the two buildings silhouetted against the distant skyline.

The map alongside shows the final approach to where the treasure was hidden.

The number of standing fence posts to the east from the fallen tree to count was the primary digit of Date 1. Date 1 was 1870, so:

Primary digit of 1870 = 1+8+7+0 = 16, 1+6 = **7 fence posts**.

A map of the whole hunt is shown below:

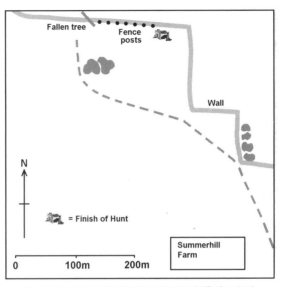

Reproduced from Ordnance Survey based mapping on behalf of The Controller of Her Majesty's Stationery Office © Crown Copyright 2004 100032058

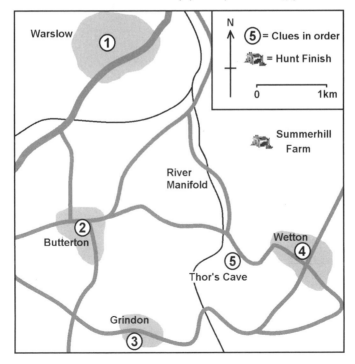

Solution II: Hathersage

Starting from the Youth Hostel, the next road to the left "owned by a rock star" is **Jagger's Lane**. The guns which "point the way up the next road" are the cannons at the entrance to a road called "Cannon fields", shown below:

The road to go up is Cogger's Lane, and the plaque in question is eventually found at the junction with Birley Lane.

The name of the building which used to be here is **GEER GREEN SCHOOL**. The year it started operating, Date 1, was **1718**. The plaque (right) also mentions that the school in question appears as the school in the village of "Morton" in "Jane Eyre" by Charlotte Brontë.

The public footpath which should be taken is on Birley Lane, the road directly opposite the plaque, and the building linked to Charlotte Brontë (by name only) is Brontë Cottage.

Just before you come to

IN THIS FIELD WAS THE SITE
OF
GEER GREEN SCHOOL
THE FIRST SCHOOL IN THIS AREA
1718····1808
IT APPEARS AS THE SCHOOL
IN THE VILLAGE OF "MORTON"
IN "JANE EYRE" BY
CHARLOTTE BRONTE

Brontë Cottage

Brontë   Cottage is the stile from which the next footpath should be taken.

The two words at the top of the gate, to be removed from Codeword 1, are **THE WARREN**.

Removing firstly GEER GREEN SCHOOL then THE WARREN from Codeword 1 leaves the phrase **STANDINGBROKENTREE**. This is used at the finale of the hunt.

The "sign dedicated to a campaigner" (surname to be used as the cipher codeword) was in memory of EVELYN A. **EVISON**. Her name is in the small plaque below the Peak and Northern public footpath sign

Applying EVISON as the cipher codeword to CJLLMGATXTUGPJJIOGBWGUNLAQSEEFELF gives the decoded message **GETDATEOFLITTERACTFROMBYELAWSSIGN**

Following the wall as directed, the sign in question is a National

Trust sign for Longshaw Estate OUTSEATS. On the back of the sign are the bye-laws, on which a note mentions "The Litter Act 1958".

Date 1:	1718
Plus Date 2:	+ 1958
plus "fiddle factor" 229162:	+ 229162
Leaves OS Grid Ref.	**SK232838**

This grid reference pointed to a place across the fields a few hundred metres to the east. Code-word 1 revealed STANDING BROKEN TREE, so the treasure was originally placed at the top of the standing broken tree, close to a pond and some ruins.

The map is shown below:

The standing broken tree

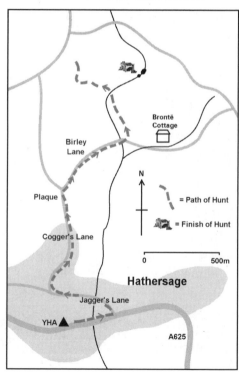

Solution 12: Rowarth

In Rowarth, the house with the "reasonable outlook", Clue 1, is **FAIR VIEW**.

The cottage "whose name implies a chess player's monarch is no longer in check", Clue 2, is **KINGSCLERE** cottage.

The house that "might have been built on a mine", Clue 3, is **COLEFIELD HOUSE**.

The white date stone on the row of cottages says "Drinkwater's Buildings **1812**". The primary digit of 1812 is $1+8+1+2 = 12$, and $1+2 = $ **3**.

Year on white date stone:	1812
Primary digit of year:	3
multiply by 50:	x 50
Gives a bearing of:	150

So the bearing to follow on the map is **150 degrees**, approximately SSE. The nearest pub is the **Little Mill Inn**, close by and to the south of Rowarth. It has a waterwheel.

The Little Mill Inn

The landlord's name is Christopher **BARNES** – Clue 4. If you inquire within you will find that the name of the Parrot is **JACK** – to be used later as the Cipher Codeword.

Clue 1	F	A	I	R	V	I	E	W		
Clue 4							B	A	R	N	E	S
Clue 2				K	I	N	G	S	C	L	E	R	E
Clue 3	C	O	L	E	F	I	E	L	D	H	O	U	S	E

The completed Word Grid

The next destination is read from the highlighted column, and is the village of **WASH**, about 5 miles from Rowarth at a bearing of about 150 degrees.

Going from the central car parking area of Wash up the hill to the east you will see **Hill Cottage**, having a date stone just above its entrance door canopy showing the year 1666 – that of the Great Fire of London – the "great city disaster".

Further along that road, around three-quarters of a mile further east, is **CHESTNUT CENTRE** conservation park, an Otter haven and Owl sanctuary – the "place linked with birds and mammals".

Removing firstly HILL COTTAGE then CHESTNUT CENTRE from Codeword 1 leaves **SCOOBY DOO** – the star of a 2002 film!

Following the road in question leads to the tiny village of Malcoff, on the edge of which there is a house with a stone bust that bears a striking similarity to Scooby Doo.

Now, using the discovered Cipher Codeword JACK to decode the given

letters using the Codeword Cipher routine shown on pages 7 and 8, the solution becomes:

TAKEFPAFTERWATERTROUGHXBRIDGETREASINCRACKATSWCORN EROFRUIN

When put in plain English, this becomes "Take footpath after water trough, cross bridge, treasure in crack at south-west corner of ruin".

Soon after Scooby Doo, carrying on the road to the west, there is a water trough on the left-hand side of the road. A few yards further on is a signed footpath also on the left-hand side of the road. Following this path leads down towards the river at which point you can see the ruin in question, which the path leads directly past.

The treasure codeword was originally placed in a crack above head height on the rightmost (south-west) corner of the ruin. A map of the whole hunt is shown below:

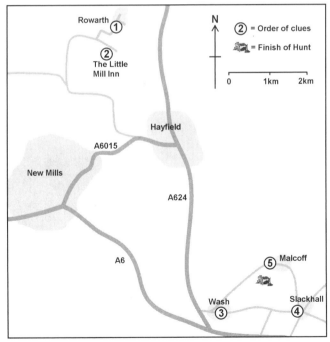

Solution 13: Hollinsclough

In Hollinsclough the building with the bell tower is the **Wheldon School**. The date stone is just under the roof of the gable, and reads **1840**. (This is Date 1.)

The earlier date stone (Date 2) is on the Methodist

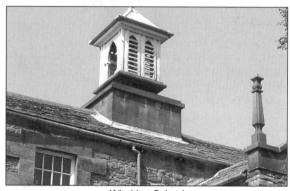

Wheldon School

Chapel, which reads **1801**. Therefore the grid reference of the next location is as follows:

Date 1:	1840
Date 2:	+ 1801
Add the fiddle factor:	+088030
= OS Grid Ref:	**SK091671**

The grid reference SK091671 takes us to the centre of the nearby village of **EARL STERNDALE**.

The name of the Prince is **HENRY BERRISFORD**, found on the war memorial column in the church graveyard. (Bud Abbott and Lou Costello were the comedy partnership referred to.)

The "sign in the area" is the sign of the village pub, the Quiet Woman. The wording on it is SOFT WORDS TURNETH AWAY WRATH, so **SOFT WORDS** repel anger. The two words to fit Clue 2 are **QUIET WOMAN**.

Removing HENRY BERRISFORD and SOFT WORDS from Code-word 1 leaves **GLUTTON GRANGE**, the next location, which doubles up as **Clue 1** on the Word Grid. It's on the OS map, half a km to the west of Earl Sterndale.

Glutton Grange is a farm. The date stone is a white circle at the top of the front wall of the main building and reads **1675**. Removing the even digit (a 6) from 1675 leaves a bearing of 175 degrees. The next destination is on this bearing "less than 5km away as the crow flies" – **LONGNOR**.

The "south-facing public place with a fruity name" (Clue 3) is **THE GRAPES HOTEL**, located in the central square of Longnor.

The café "that is, to be blunt, a reddish colour" (Clue 4) is **F R A N K L Y SCARLETT**.

The place with a sign containing a silhouetted animal (Clue 5) is the **RED BULL GALLERY**.

The place to cure children's toys (Clue 6) is the **DOLLS HOSPITAL**.

Frankly Scarlett

The house with a flowery name (Clue 7) is **BLUEBELL COTTAGE**.

The ivy-covered dwelling with its name on the door knocker (Clue 8) is **SHEFFIELD HOUSE**.

The metropolitan police were formed in 1829. **LEIGH COTTAGE** (Clue 9) has a date stone showing this year.

The "seasonally named house" (Clue 10) is **SPRING COTTAGE**.

The house "with a wooden name plaque referring to a metallic outlook" (Clue 11) is **COPPERHILL VIEW**.

The house "which may collect silver" (Clue 12) is **MAGPIE COTTAGE** and the house "which may not charge for lodging" (Clue 13) is **INNISFREE**.

The locations of the clues within Longnor are shown overleaf.

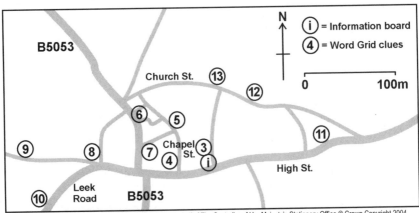

Reproduced from Ordnance Survey based mapping on behalf of The Controller of Her Majesty's Stationery Office © Crown Copyright 2004

Reading down the highlighted column, the next destination is **BEGGARS BRIDGE**. (This is marked on the OS map and crosses the River Dove northeast of Longnor.)

The information board is just outside the Grapes Hotel in the main village square. The text reads "Longnor, once a thriving market town, lies at a northern point of the Staffordshire Moorlands close to the Derbyshire boundary, in the Peak District National Park. It is sited on a high ridge dividing the rivers Dove and Manifold, close to ancient trade routes. Early village history is unclear, but there are records of activity in the area from the days of Saxon Kings of Mercia around 700AD."

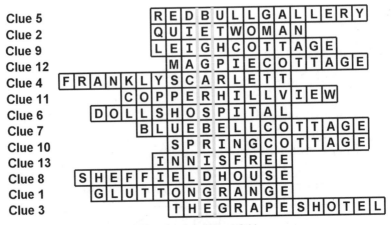

The completed Word Grid

Using the Key Counted Hidden Clue routine on the text above reveals **GONETILLHORIZBELOWTREASATBASEOFTREE**. (Go north-east until you see the horizon below. Treasure is at the base of the tree.) Proceed to Beggar's Bridge, about 1km north-east of the centre of Longnor (and marked on the OS map) to continue.

If you walk up the path to the north-east from Beggar's Bridge you will see the following horizon to the west after about 100 metres:

This is where the horizon matches the silhouette. At this point is a small tree. The treasure codeword was found at the base of the trunk of this tree, just under a rock. A map of the complete hunt is shown below:

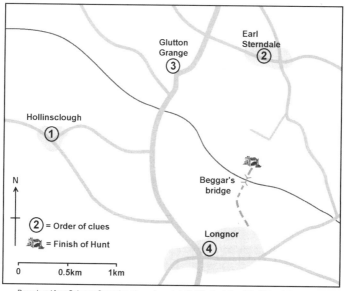

Solution 14: Curbar Edge

The "rock that shows seventy-eight minutes from the turn of the day" is carved with ISAIAH 1:18. (01:18 is seventy-eight minutes after midnight.)

Using **ISAIAH** as the cipher code-word for the Codeworded Cipher gives

GODOWNRDONEMTURNLEFTONMAINRDUNTILFIRSTPUB

(Go down the road one mile, turn left until first pub.) The pub in question is in Baslow and is the **RUTLAND ARMS**.

Within the Rutland arms, the framed photograph in question is above the pool table. **HOLBROOK'S SAUCE** is advertised under *Pearson's Weekly*.

Removing firstly ISIAIAH then HOLBROOKS SAUCE from Code-word 1 leaves Location A, **EDENSOR**.

Within the Word Grid, Clue 1 is **SYCAMORE COTTAGE**. The "large reference to a former Coronation Street character" is a large date stone on the balcony of a house further up the road saying ALMA 1854.

The cottage with an owl on the name sign (Clue 2) is **NAILSTONE COTTAGE**.

The house with a couple of round windows (Clue 3) is **THE CORNER HOUSE**.

The house with a balcony

The house whose name is related to water (Clue 4) is **HYDRO COTTAGE**. The large dwelling with a gravel drive (Clue 5) is **BAR HOUSE**.

The Prince Regent reigned as George IV from 1820-1830. Therefore the dwelling built when the Prince Regent reigned as monarch (Clue 6) is **LADYWELL COTTAGE** – dated 1824.

The house where someone who is neither a carnivore nor an omnivore now lives (Clue 7) is **YELDSIDE COTTAGE** (a plaque on the house says 'A vegetarian lives here').

The house with the tree-lined drive (Clue 8) is **TITHE PASTURES**.

Clue 9, "a house with a reference to cooking with eggs" is **SUNNYSIDE**.

Clue 8	T I T H E P A S T U R E S
Clue 4	H Y D R O C O T T A G E
Clue 7	Y E L D S I D E C O T T A G E
Clue 6	L A D Y W E L L C O T T A G E
Clue 1	S Y C A M O R E C O T T A G E
Clue 2	N A I L S T O N E C O T T A G E
Clue 3	T H E C O R N E R H O U S E
Clue 5	B A R H O U S E
Clue 9	S U N N Y S I D E

The completed Word Grid

At Location A (previously found to be EDENSOR), there is a sign in the church porch entitled "To our American friends". This states that the grave of **KATHLEEN CAVENDISH** (d. 1948), formerly Kathleen Kennedy, sister of President J.F Kennedy is found amongst the Cavendish family graves at the top of the graveyard. This is the "person who became more famous by association after she died" (when he became President).

Removing this name from Codeword 2 leaves the NAME as **JIM BOYACK**.

The name on the highlighted column in the Word Grid is **SOLYMOSSY**. Inside the church is a book listing the graves, and the date next to the longest name is 3rd June 1975.

Using this to get the next grid reference:

Date in DDMMYY format: 030675
plus "fiddle factor":   + 211036
= OS Grid Ref: **SK241711**

SK241711 takes the hunter to the nearby village of **PILSLEY**. The village of Pilsley contains the Devonshire Arms pub:

The information board within "relating to an inverted image of a bygone day" was subtitled "**Reflections of yesterday**" and starts

"Welcome to the Devonshire Arms, in the most delightful village of Pilsley, on the magnificent Chatsworth Estate. The earliest reference to Pilsley appears in the Domesday Book of 1086, nearly a thousand years ago, as Pirelaie. The parish of Edensor which included Pilsley belonged to Henry de Ferrars at this period. It later passed to the Foljambes family."

When the given key is applied to it, the plaque is decoded to:

INCHATSWTHGRNDSISBENCHFORNAME

Loosely translated it means 'In Chatsworth Grounds is a Bench for (dedicated to) NAME' where NAME is that found earlier – JIM BOYACK.

The bench in question is in the grounds (but not the garden), close to the river and the entrance, around 300 metres north of the road bridge. Behind the bench are two trees, one of which hid the treasure codeword.

A map of the complete hunt is shown below:

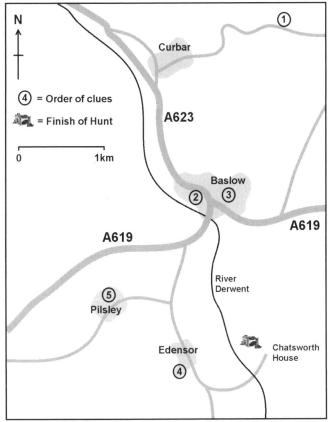

Solution 15: Goyt Valley

The "prominent feature on the wall of the road" is **the Shrine**. This is marked on the OS map. Within the Shrine there are a couple of Latin phrases. However, the only one found in Codeword 1 is **GRATIA PLENA**.

The "green door of convenience" is a public convenience and the "building with 4 windows behind a barrier" is the dam control house for Errwood reservoir dam.

The nearby post box has **CATCH RETURNS** written upon it.

Removing firstly GRATIA PLENA then CATCH RETURNS from Codeword 1 leaves **TAXAL**, the next destination. This is a small village around 4km to the north.

In Taxal, you should soon find the gravel road with the house at the end having a bell-shaped sign. This house is Clue 1 – **THE CHIMES**.

The "prominent local building with an information board" is the church and the character referred to was Michael Heathcote, an 18th-century "Gentleman of the Pantry and Yeoman of the Mouth" (Royal Taster!) The year he died (Treasure Location Date 1) was **1768**.

On the east-facing outside wall of the church is the "dedication to someone who provided many years of service". This is a stone plaque to the Rev. S. Evans, who gave service from 1886-1922.

Therefore the compass bearing is calculated as follows:

Last year of service:		1922
first year of service:	–	1886
years of service:		36
multiply by 7.5:	x	7.5
= bearing:		**270**

This gives a bearing of **270 degrees**, which is due west. On the OS map, the closest church on this bearing is **Kettleshulme church**.

The house immediately to the right of Kettleshulme church is called Brooklands, which is an anagram of "blank doors". It has a plaque upon the front wall, saying "1824 rebuilt 1870". Therefore Treasure Location Date 2 is **1870.**

The house on the corner is Clue 2, **SPONDS VIEW**, and its date stone, Treasure Location Date 3, is **2001**.

The house with the black name sign "which could be a refuge for a certain type of tree", Clue 3, is **BIRCH HAVEN**.

Robert Banks Jenkinson was the British Prime Minister from 1812-1827, so Clue 4 is **PADDOCK LODGE**, with a date stone of 1823.

The house to the right across the junction with the house name built into a wall (Clue 5) is **BANCROFTS**.

Clue 6 is **STOCKS BANK**.

The house after the old school (Clue 7) is **FLYFOLD COTTAGE**.

The "literary building on the right with a date stone" is the library, and the date stone (Treasure Location Date 4) is **1876**.

Clue 4						P	A	D	D	O	C	K	L	O	D	G	E
Clue 7							F	L	Y	F	O	L	D	C	O	T	T	A	G	E
Clue 8	D	A	L	E	S	F	A	R	M	H	O	U	S	E
Clue 1							T	H	E	C	H	I	M	E	S
Clue 3					B	I	R	C	H	H	A	V	E	N
Clue 6		S	T	O	C	K	S	B	A	N	K
Clue 2		S	P	O	N	D	S	V	I	E	W
Clue 5				B	A	N	C	R	O	F	T	S

The completed Word Grid

The house with the old-style lamp above the door (Clue 8) is **DALES FARMHOUSE**.

The next destination (high-lighted column) is **PYM CHAIR**. This is marked on the OS map and is on the brow of a hill approximately 3km along the C road to the south. A large sign theorises on the origin of its name.

The building in a westerly direction sheltered by trees is Jenkin Chapel, named on the OS map.

Across the road, the sign dedicates the footpath to LIL ALMOND, "a Canadian lover

Jenkin Chapel

of the English countryside". The first number at the top of this sign is **161**. Calculating the mileage to the next destination:

First number on sign:	161
subtract 132:	−132
=	29
divide by 10 = mileage:	**2.9 miles**

So the hunter must travel for **2.9 miles** on the mileometer **in the direction of the date stone, when looking towards it from this sign**. This is back along the road towards Pym Chair.

After 2.9 miles, there is a car park for the south side of Errwood reservoir. At the back of the car park is an information board about the Goyt valley with an extended part showing a woodland walk around **Errwood Hall ruins**. The largest black area on the sign is that of the actual ruins, so the ruins are the final destination.

The information plaque at Errwood Hall ruins explains that the Coal mine operated until **1929** (Treasure Location Date 5) and that the Shrine was built in **1889** (Treasure Location Date 6).

The hunt says to "stand underneath the middle one of three in a row". This referred to the three arches on the left of the ruins.

The path of the paces

So, from the middle of the three arches in a row, face inwards and count out metres (= paces) as follows:

Forwards <primary digit of Treasure Location Date 4 > = 1+8+7+6 => 22 => 2+2 = **4 paces**,

turn left and count <primary digit of Treasure Location Date 1> = 1+7+6+8 => 22 => 2+2 = **4 paces**,

turn left again and count <primary digit of Treasure Location Date 5> = 1+9+2+9 => 21 => 2+1 = **3 paces**,

turn right and count <primary digit of Treasure Location Date 3> 4 = 2+0+0+1 = **3 paces**,

turn right again and count <primary digit of Treasure Location Date 6> 5 = 1+8+8+9 => 26 => 2+6 = **8 paces**,

turn left and count <primary digit of Treasure Location Date 2> = 1+8+7+0 => 16 => 1+6 = **7 paces**.

A map of the whole hunt is shown overleaf.

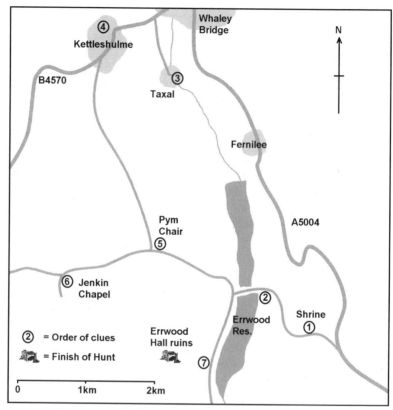

Solution 16: Peak Forest

The name of the tree "propagated from another" is the **MILLENNIUM YEW**. It was a new planting for the millennium and can be found on the right-hand side of the churchyard close to the church. It was planted on 12th March 2000, which makes a six-digit number of 120300.

Date in DDMMYY format:	120300
plus "fiddle factor":	+ 54512
gives OS Grid Ref.	**SK174812**

SK174812 is close to the centre of **BRADWELL**, one of the larger Peak District villages to the north-west of Peak Forest.

The "building with 4 columns" is the Methodist Church, and the highest date thereon" (Date 1) is **1807**.

The house "named after a group of pedigree dogs" (Clue 1 in the Word Grid) is **POINTERS**.

The house name "possibly referring to drab monks" (Clue 2) is **GREYFRIARS**.

The "house with 2 chimney stacks and an unusual old rock name plate" (Clue 3) is **ROCK HILL COTTAGE**.

The house "with a circular name stone" is Millstone Cottage and the house after it (Clue 4) is **WESTCOTE**.

Further up the road, the house "whose name suggests a decent outlook over the dale" (Clue 5) is **HOPE VALLEY VIEW**, which indeed commands a fine view of the Hope Valley.

The house "named after a coloured drink of olden days" (Clue 6) is **GREYMEAD**.

The house with the wooden lattice around the door (Clue 7) is **CASULA**.

The building linked with a youth movement is the 1ˢᵗ Bradwell Scout Group Headquarters and Bunkhouse. The date in question – Date 2, is carved into the rock just above the sign and is **1754**.

The house which has an unusual chimney pot (Clue 8) is **WEAVERS COTTAGE**.

The later Victorian date from the chapel (Date 3) is **1878**.

The house name "on the entrance to a long drive on the left" (Clue 9) is **GLEN VIEW**.

The large white building (Clue 10) is **WHITE HART** – a pub.

The date upon it (Date 4) is **1676**.

The house that "could have been named after a cat" is **TOM COTTAGE**.

The filled-in Word Grid is shown below:

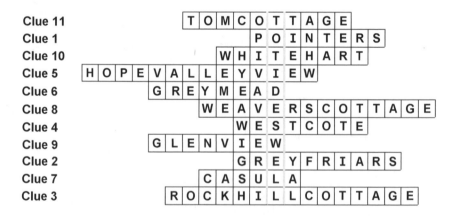

Clue 11				T	O	M	C	O	T	T	A	G	E	
Clue 1							P	O	I	N	T	E	R	S
Clue 10					W	H	I	T	E	H	A	R	T	
Clue 5	H	O	P	E	V	A	L	L	E	Y	V	I	E	W
Clue 6				G	R	E	Y	M	E	A	D			
Clue 8					W	E	A	V	E	R	S	C	O	T	T	A	G	E
Clue 4					W	E	S	T	C	O	T	E		
Clue 9			G	L	E	N	V	I	E	W				
Clue 2					G	R	E	Y	F	R	I	A	R	S
Clue 7				C	A	S	U	L	A					
Clue 3			R	O	C	K	H	I	L	L	C	O	T	T	A	G	E

The highlighted column shows that "the next place to go" is **TO TIDESWELL!**

You should already have found the 4 dates that can now be used to find where to start the Word Search. These were:

Date 1: 1807

Date 2: 1754

Date 3: 1878

Date 4: 1676

Number to start (across) = Primary digit of 1807 + Primary digit of 1754. = 7+8 = **15**.

Number to start (down) = Primary digit of 1878 + Primary digit of 1676. = 6+2 = **8**.

The solution to the Word Search, starting from 15 across and 8 down, is:

The Word Search therefore reads:

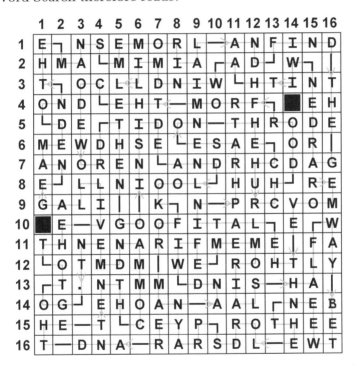

REMOVE THE LATIN PHRASE ON THE CHURCH DOOR FROM THE CODEWORD THEN GO INSIDE AND LOOK FOR MAN AND WIFE MEMORIALS HALF WAY BETWEEN THE LORDS PRAYER AND THE TENTH COMMANDMENT. GO TO THE VILLAGE NAMED ON THE MANS MEMORIAL AND FIND THE GARDEN WITH A WINDMILL

The church in question was Tideswell's "cathedral" church, the parish church of St John the Baptist.

The church at Tideswell

The Latin phrase on the front doors is **QUAM DILECTA TABERNACULA**.

On opposing inside walls of Tideswell church are the Lord's Prayer and The Ten Commandments. On the floor down one of the aisles between them is a memorial plate dedicated to Frank Middleton, and the village named on his memorial was **WHESTON**, about a mile west of Tideswell.

In Wheston, there is a garden with a small stone windmill. The house name is **VALDONA**.

Removing MILLENNIUM YEW (found at Peak Forest Church), QUAM DILECTA TABERNACULA (on Tideswell church doors) and finally VALDONA from Codeword 1 leaves **WORMHILL** (a small village about 2km south-west of Wheston).

In Wormhill, the 18th-century pioneer was James Brindley and the metal plaque is found next to a prominent water feature – the Brindley memorial, which backs onto the main road through the village.

The Brindley monument in Wormhill

The text on the plaque reads:

James Brindley was born at Tunstead in this parish in 1716. His ability to solve difficult problems of engineering earned him a reputation which led to his appointment as Engineer for the Bridgewater canal from Worsley to Manchester. Opened in 1761 this was the first arterial canal and its commercial success ushered in the canal era.

Combined with the given key, this translates to:

Find the building in Litton adorned with a cherub and take the date of the small structure it faces.

So on to **LITTON**, around 3km to the east. The School building in the centre of Litton has the carved cherub just above the left set of windows.

The school faces the bus shelter and this has AD1984 carved on its roof. So Date 5 is **1984**.

The primary digit of 1984 = 1+9+8+4 = 22, 2+2 = 4. 15 x 4 = **60 degrees**. The next village as the crow flies on a bearing of 60 degrees is **FOOLOW**. The bench in question is against a wall facing the Saxon Cross, and is dedicated by **MIZPAH**.

The Saxon Cross in the centre of Foolow

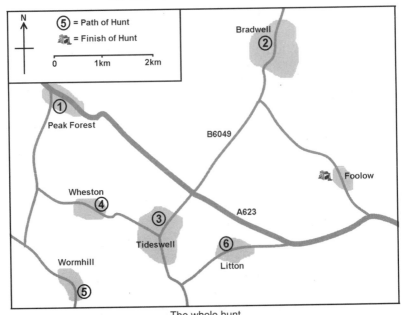

The whole hunt

Hunter's Notes

Jot down your notes on these blank pages as a personal record!

Hunter's Notes

Hunter's Notes

Hunter's Notes

Also from Sigma Leisure:

Rocky Rambles in The Peak District

Fred Broadhurst

"The Peak District has a dramatic story to tell and Fred Broadhurst is just the guide we need." - Aubrey Manning, presenter of the BBC TV series 'Earth Story'.

You don't have to be an expert or even an amateur geologist to enjoy these 'rocky rambles'! Where better than in and around the Peak District would you find geology right there beneath your feet - all you need to know is where to look. Detailed maps are included plus information about parking facilities, and the all-important venues for refreshments along the way. The comprehensive glossary of terms, which covers the identification of Peak District Rocks, forms an invaluable supplement and provides 'at a glance' information for the reader.
£8.95

Tea Shop Walks in The Peak District

Norman and June Buckley

Easy walks that are ideal for all the family – and perfect for long sunny days, with the reward of a welcome break at a traditional tea shop in delightful surroundings. This well-established book was checked and updated in 2003 by Popular walking duo Norman and June Buckley – who are quickly becoming the country's tea shop experts. "...the shape of things to come...highly recommended" *The Congleton Chronicle. £6.95*

Peak District Walking – On The Level

Norman Buckley

Some folk prefer easy walks, and sometimes there's just not time for an all-day yomp. In either case, this is definitely a book to keep on your bookshelf. Norman Buckley has already had considerable success with "On The Level" books for the Lake District and the Yorkshire Dales - with each title in the series reprinted several times.

The walks are ideal for family outings and the precise instructions ensure that there's little chance of losing your way. Well-produced maps encourage everybody to try out the walks - all of which are well scattered across the Peak District. *£7.95*

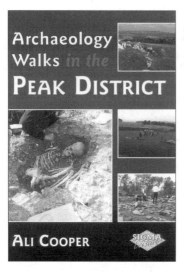

Archaeology Walks in The Peak District
Ali Cooper

These walks explore archaeological sites where there are visible pre-historic features in the landscape: Bronze age barrows, stone circles, caves, mines and much more. Walks are from 3 to 12 miles and are fully illustrated. The book includes an introduction to the study of archaeology and a glossary of the terminology used. Brief descriptions of the major finds on the walks are included, plus a bibliography for those who wish to delve deeper. Ali Cooper has an MA in archaeology and is a keen outdoors enthusiast. *£6.95*

Best Pub Walks in the Dark Peak
&
Best Pub Walks in the White Peak

These two books, both by Les Lumsdon and Martin Smith, provide comprehensive coverage of the entire Peak District. Inspiring walks and welcoming pubs enable walkers to appreciate the history, landscape and personalities of the area. These books were published by us originally in the 1980s and have recently been completely updated to ensure accuracy. Each book costs *£7.95*.

All-Terrain Pushchair Walks: Peak District
Karen Cosgrove

Following the success of our 'All-Terrain Pushchair Walks' books for the Lake District, this companion edition includes level routes around Peak District villages to the more adventurous (but safe) hikes across the moors. Karen is a parent of a young child and has an excellent knowledge of the Peak District. So now there's no reason to stay at home – here is the ideal opportunity to introduce the youngest children to the wide-open spaces of the Peak District! *£7.95 (due late 2004)*

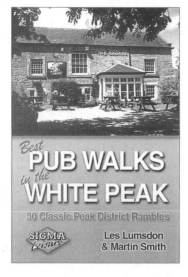